HAND TOOLS
AND TECHNIQUES

Hand Tools
and Techniques

Bob Wearing

Aidan Walker
Series Editor

ARGUS BOOKS

Argus Books Limited
Wolsey House
Wolsey Road
Hemel Hempstead
Hertfordshire HP2 4SS
England

First published by Argus Books 1988
© Robert Wearing 1988

ISBN 0 85242 954 1

Phototypesetting by Goodfellow & Egan, Cambridge.
Printed and bound by LR Printing Services Ltd, Manor Royal, Crawley, West Sussex, RH10 2QN, England.

CONTENTS

INTRODUCTION

In spite of the development over the years of all types of machine tools, the principles and techniques of using hand tools remain at the heart of woodworking. Although machine tools work both quicker and cheaper, they rarely produce the kind of result obtained from using hand tools. For example the machine planer cannot match the finish of good hand planing, nor can machine-made dovetails compare with well spaced and hand cut dovetails.

Inevitably in a book of this size selections had to be made. I have omitted numerous tools whose wooden forms have been superseded by metal and whose production has ceased. These are for the collector rather than the worker at the bench. The impact of the small power router has been enormous; it is now economically priced, well within the range even of many amateur workers, and consequently a number of the hand tools it replaces have been omitted.

For many years the skills and technology of hand tools were taught in schools as part of GCE and CSE courses in woodwork. Those achieving 'A' levels had by that time acquired a high degree of skill and knowledge of hand tools. Sadly this is now of the past. 'Basic skills' are neither required nor taught yet increasing numbers of adults, both men and women, find pleasure in working wood, quite apart from any financial needs. More and more houses now have garages, providing reasonable workshop facilities. Yet often their only means of acquiring information is by either a two hour, once a week evening class, if one is accessible, or from books.

It is hoped that this book and others in the series will supply the information once available in schools and start keen amateurs and possibly young apprentices on the right lines.

ACKNOWLEDGEMENTS

I appreciate the help given in supplying some of the illustrations by Record Marples, Stanley and Eclipse Tools and by the Editor of Woodworker in permitting me to reuse material previously published there.

Robert Wearing, 1988

CHAPTER 1

SHARPENING EDGE TOOLS

All edge tools are sharpened in much the same way though, of course, there are individual differences. There are two stages. The first is grinding, the putting on of the basic bevel. The second is honing, sometimes called sharpening, which is the putting on of a keen edge by means of a second very small fine bevel.

Grinding was formerly carried out on large natural stones, running vertically in a trough of water, turned either by hand, foot or latterly by electricity. This is now seldom the method of the amateur or the small craftsman. A recent development has been the small horizontally running water cooled stones, a smaller version of professional oil cooled stones. These very much fill a need. They are economical in both cost and space. Suitable guides and tool-holders guarantee success with minimal skill. New models are constantly appearing. High-speed grinders, intended primarily for engineering, are commonly used. They are narrow, seldom wider than an inch. Six inches is a useful diameter. The greatest care must be taken not to overheat the tool as this destroys the hardness. Frequent dipping-out in water is necessary.

The life cycle of a cutting edge follows

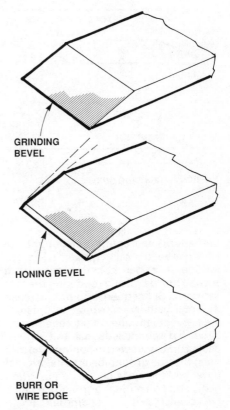

GRINDING BEVEL

HONING BEVEL

BURR OR WIRE EDGE

Fig. 1.1

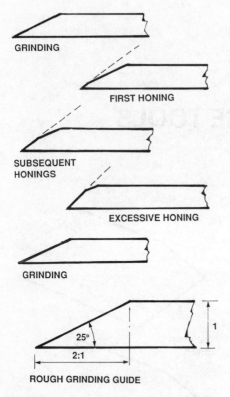

GRINDING

FIRST HONING

SUBSEQUENT HONINGS

EXCESSIVE HONING

GRINDING

25° 2:1 1

ROUGH GRINDING GUIDE

Fig. 1.2

on both grinding and honing being negligible.

Sharpening can be greatly facilitated by the use of a honing tool. There should be no indignity in using this. It makes a first class job, reduces the amount of grinding and is particularly useful on edges which are narrow or which have to remain absolutely square.

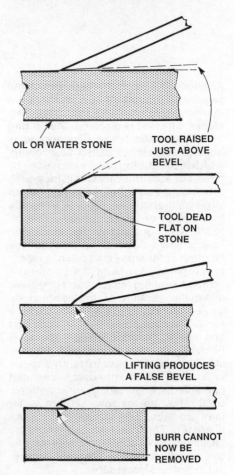

OIL OR WATER STONE

TOOL RAISED JUST ABOVE BEVEL

TOOL DEAD FLAT ON STONE

LIFTING PRODUCES A FALSE BEVEL

BURR CANNOT NOW BE REMOVED

Fig. 1.3

the pattern illustrated. When bought, the edge has been ground only, so it is not fit for use. It is then honed, putting on a second fine bevel and rendering the tool fit for use. Subsequent honings increase the angle of the honing bevel and also its area. Eventually the angle becomes so large that keenness is lost and a great deal of time is wasted in honing. The tool must then be ground back to its original bevel and the cycle begun again. When good and convenient grinding facilities are available it is recommended to grind almost every time, the time spent

8

Honing can be carried out on the traditional oilstone or on that recent arrival, the Japanese water stone. Oilstones can be man-made or natural. Popular and economically priced man-made stones are the 'India' by Norton in the fine and medium grades, or the Carborundum. 8 × 2 × 1 in. is the commonly accepted size for a bench stone. Natural stones – the Arkansas and the Washita – produce very fine edges but are both slow cutting and very expensive. The stone should be housed in a wooden box which is nowadays built up rather than cut from the solid. A small end grain block at each end permits the full length of the stone to be used. Water stones must be kept wet. A narrow plastic freezer box makes a good container with an old squeezy bottle for the water. Water stones are quite soft, which makes them unsuitable for communal workshops. Their cleanliness is a major advantage. As stones wear hollow they can be rubbed flat on a sheet of plate

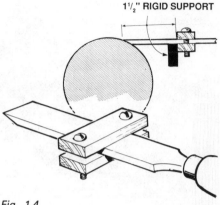

1¹/₂" RIGID SUPPORT

Fig. 1.4

glass. For oilstones, use water and aluminium oxide lapping compound by Carborundum which is available as coarse, medium and fine, to suit the particular oilstone. For water stones, use wet and dry abrasive paper working from a coarse to the finer grits.

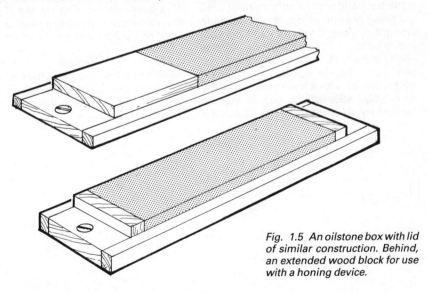

Fig. 1.5 An oilstone box with lid of similar construction. Behind, an extended wood block for use with a honing device.

Fig. 1.6 Eclipse honing guide, stepped to take chisels or plane blades.

Having oiled or wet the stone, place the tool on, slowly lifting the handle until the bevel is flat on the surface. This is the position when the oil or water oozes out under the cutting edge. Raise the tool minutely. This is the honing position. Hone back and forth in this manner until the finest burr or wire edge can be seen along the entire edge. Reverse the tool and lay it *dead flat* on the stone – this is vitally important. Hone this way until the wire edge bends upward and repeat both processes for a few strokes until the wire edge falls off. It can finally be cleared by stroking the edge through a piece of end grain wood, preferably not hand held. The edge can be finished by stropping on leather glued to a wood strip and treated with fine valvegrinding paste from a garage. The flat side of the tool must stay completely flat. Any trace of a bevel developing on the flat side makes it impossible to remove the wire edge without further increasing the false bevel.

This is the method for sharpening chisels and the square cutters of rebate and shoulder planes. Variations of the method will be described under the individual tools.

CHAPTER 2

PLANES AND PLANING

BENCH PLANES

Discounting the wooden planes, of which there is now only a limited production and no general interest, there are three fully adjustable bench planes in cast iron.

(a) The jack plane, cutter widths 2 in. and 2⅜ in. and lengths 14 and 15 in., is the general purpose plane, whose main use is preparing components to size. Its cutter is sharpened on the oilstone to a very gentle curve, thus ensuring that the corners do not dig in and cause a step in the planed surface.

(b) The smoothing plane is made with cutter widths of 1¾, 2 and 2⅜ in. and lengths respectively of 8, 9 and 10 in. The 2⅜ in. is favoured by joiners, the 2 in. is most commonly chosen by cabinet makers while the 1¾ in. suits youngsters, beginners and anyone working on smaller, finer work. It is, as the name implies, a finishing and cleaning up plane, used in the final stages and removing negligible thickness. To avoid leaving a shallow fluted surface, it is sharpened virtually straight and square with just the corners eased away.

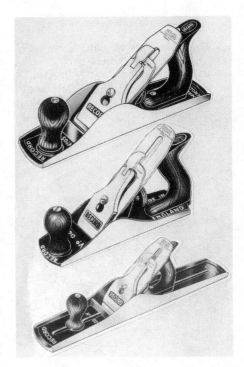

Fig. 2.1 Record planes, from top to bottom jack plane, smoothing plane and try plane.

11

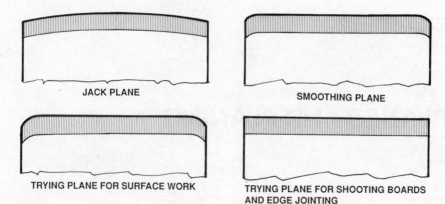

JACK PLANE

SMOOTHING PLANE

TRYING PLANE FOR SURFACE WORK

TRYING PLANE FOR SHOOTING BOARDS
AND EDGE JOINTING

Fig. 2.2 Grinding forms for plane irons.

(c) The trying plane, with a cutter of 2⅜ or 2⅝ in. and a length of 22 in. is, as the name originally meant, a trueing plane. The greater length makes for more accurate planing of edges for jointing (hence its alterna-tive name, Jointer) or large flat surfaces. For surface work it is sharpened like the smoother. For work on edges and for use on the shooting board (see page 00), it can be sharpened quite straight and

Fig. 2.3 Plane nomenclature

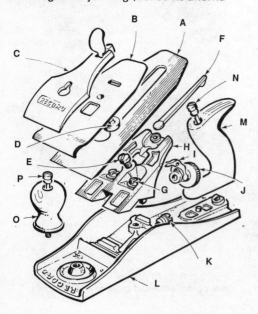

A – BLADE
B – CAP IRON
C – LEVER CAP
D – CAP IRON SCREW
E – LEVER CAP SCREW
F – LATERAL LEVER
G – FROG SCREW
H – FROG
I – Y LEVER
J – CUTTER ADJUSTING WHEEL
K – FROG ADJUSTING SCREW
L – BODY
M – HANDLE
N – NUT AND SCREW FOR HANDLE
O – KNOB
P – NUT AND SCREW FOR KNOB

square, hence it is a good idea to have two blades for this plane.

A less common model is the Fore or Panel plane which is 18 in. long with a 2⅜ in. cutter.

Almost the sole survivor of the family of wooden planes is the wood jack plane. This still has a following. There must be quite a number of serious workers with whom this remains a firm favourite. However, since most schools have long since discontinued using them and are equipped with metal planes, a generation has emerged having no experience of the wooden jack, so like others of the wooden planes, the jack can be considered doomed. Its claimed advantages are an almost indestructibility and sweeter running on the wood. (This latter is debatable when the iron plane is used with an oilpad.) Its critics cite the less convenient method of adjustment, by hammer, the length of time required to grind and sharpen the thick blade, the lack of a comfortable front grip and the handle set high above the work. To this must be added the occasional planing true of the sole and the less frequent re-mouthing. Planing narrow edges wears the sole excessively in the middle making this trueing up necessary.

Cut is increased by striking the blade. It is decreased by striking the top of the fore part of the body. The better planes had a striking button let in at this point.

ADJUSTING

The first and least often used adjustment is the size of mouth. With the blade removed, the two frog screws are slackened and the frog or bed can now be moved backwards or forwards by its adjusting screw. The frog screws are then re-tightened. A larger mouth permits rapid removal of wood with a coarse cut but a poor finish. A fine or

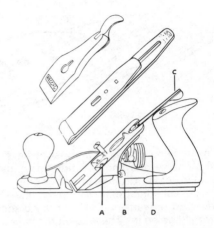

Fig. 2.4 Metal plane adjustments. A & B mouth, C lateral blade movement, D depth of cut.

close mouth permits only a fine shaving but gives a good finish. For a start, set a jackplane's mouth to about 1/32 in. and a smoother and try-plane 1/64 in. or less. Attempting too fine a mouth will cause clogging but will not be alone in creating this effect.

The cut, that is the thickness of shaving removed, is controlled by the brass adjusting nut operating the 'Y' lever which in turn operates in a slot in the cap iron, to which the blade is attached. Clockwise increases the cut. After reducing the cut, the last adjustment must always be a clockwise one to take up the slack in the mechanism. Naturally, a

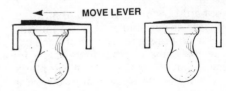

Fig. 2.5 Lateral adjustment.

Fig. 2.6 Setting of the cap iron or breaker.

fine shaving produces a superior finish to a coarse one and two fine shavings involve less effort than one thick one.

The last adjustment is with the lateral lever, to prevent one side of the blade from 'digging in'. The stud on the lateral lever must engage in the slot of the blade. This must always be checked when assembling the plane. The lever cap screw is commonly kept too tight. When correctly tight it should be just possible with the fingers, not the lateral lever, to slightly move the blade sideways.

To simplify, the function of the cap iron (in America this is called the Breaker) is to destroy the strength of the shaving and so reduce tearing. A fine finishing cut demands a close set cap iron. For coarser quicker work the cap iron is set further back. Too close a cap iron combined with too fine a mouth will result in clogging. Suggestions for initial setting of the cap iron are as follows.

For rough preliminary work:
from 1/16 to 1/32 in.
For finishing work:
1/64 in.
For hardwoods with difficult grain:
as close as possible without clogging.

Having pre-set the mouth and the cap iron the plane can be made ready for use. Sight along the sole of the plane, and with the lateral lever, bring the blade symmetrical to the sole. Next, fully

withdraw the blade. Grip in the vice a piece of softwood, say 12 × 3 × 3/4 in. with its edge uppermost. Commence planing, slowly turning the brass adjusting nut until the first fine shaving results. This must be a very fine shaving. Stop here and adjust the lateral lever until this first fine shaving comes from the middle of the blade and not from either corner. Now the required amount of cut can be applied. This lateral adjustment should stay until the blade is removed or is accidentally knocked out of place.

Fig. 2.7 Stance

Fig. 2.9 Top, assisting a beginner to settle the front of the plane. Second, start of stroke, down pressure on front. Third, end of stroke, down pressure on rear. Bottom, edge grip, with fingers forming a fence.

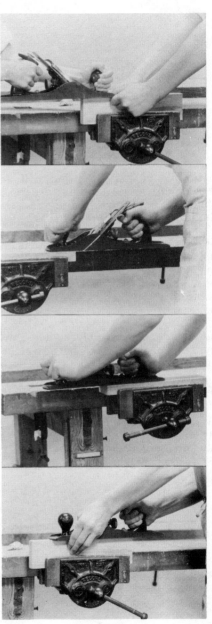

It will be obvious now why the oft repeated advice, derived from the days of wooden planes, of laying the plane on its side when not in use is quite unsound. It often results in upsetting the carefully adjusted lateral setting. A far better method is to park the plane on a wood strip covered with lightly oiled felt. This has the triple advantage of not disturbing the setting, lightly lubricating the sole and contributing to rust prevention.

On this same edge, practise planing, aiming with each stroke to obtain a full length, full width shaving. Begin by well settling the front of the plane, ie ahead of the blade. Push forward until the catch of blade is felt, pause momentarily, then

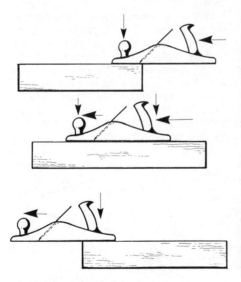

Fig. 2.8 Hand pressure, when planing.

15

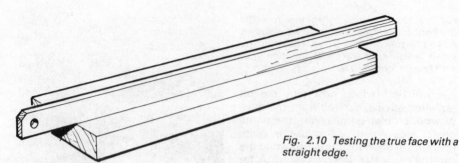

Fig. 2.10 Testing the true face with a straight edge.

push without taking a swing at it. At the commencement of the stroke there should be firm downward pressure on the front handle. The rear hand merely propels the plane forward. At the end of the stroke downward pressure is on the rear handle while the front hand maintains forward motion. In the middle of the stroke, forward and downward pressure is equally distributed between both hands.

Have the feet in a position which will be comfortable not only at the commencement of the stroke, but also at the end.

When small pieces of wood are ripped out, producing a rough surface, this is called *tearing*.

The cures for tearing
(1) Plane in the reverse direction
(2) Sharpen the blade
(3) Take a finer cut

(4) Set the cap-iron closer
(5) Set the mouth closer.

Any one of these, or any combination of any number of them, will eventually provide a cure.

PREPARING COMPONENTS TO SIZE

In preparing components to size, the first stage is to produce and test one true flat face. This is nowadays called the *true face* but was formerly referred to as the *face side*. The operation is known as *facing*.

With a jack plane, plane off the dirt and roughness from one larger face. Set the cut fine and endeavour to plane the surface hollow. Take nothing from the ends. When the plane refuses to cut any further, plane from end to end, working systematically from side to side. As soon as continuous full length shavings are obtained, *stop* and test the surface so far obtained.

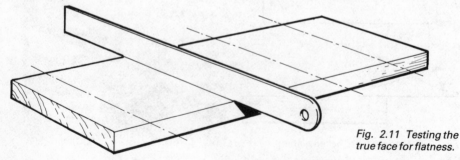

Fig. 2.11 Testing the true face for flatness.

16

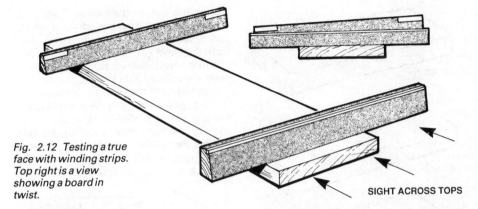

Fig. 2.12 Testing a true face with winding strips. Top right is a view showing a board in twist.

SIGHT ACROSS TOPS

Tests for a True Face

(1) Is it flat in length?
Test in several places with a straight-edge which is longer than the work.
(2) Is it flat in width?
Test in several places with a straight-edge or rule which is longer than the width.
(3) Is it 'in wind', ie twisted?
Test by sighting across a pair of winding strips (see Fig. 2.12).

Correct by taking fine shavings from the high spots being careful that in correcting for one test, the other two are not upset. When all three tests are satisfied, mark with the face mark α.

The next stage is to produce an edge exactly square (ie at right angles) to this true face. This is called *edging*.

With a fine cut, hollow the edge, taking nothing from the extreme ends, until the plane will cut no more. Now plane through from end to end until a full length full width shaving results. *Stop.* Test for accuracy.

Tests for a True Edge

(1) Is it flat in length?
Test with a straight-edge longer than the work.

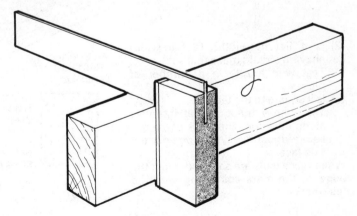

Fig. 2.13 Testing the true edge.

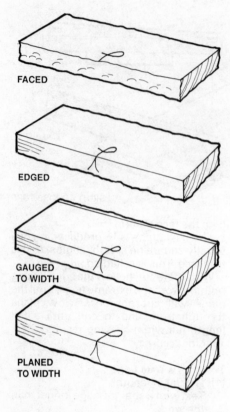

FACED

EDGED

GAUGED TO WIDTH

PLANED TO WIDTH

Fig. 2.14

Correcting an untrue edge The jack-plane cutter is sharpened to a slight curve so it follows that while shavings from the centre are of uniform thickness, shavings from either side of the plane have a thick and a thin edge.

If one side of the wood is high, *do not tilt the plane* for this will produce a second surface. Merely slide the plane over to the high side, keeping the sole flat on the existing surface, and plane full length shavings. These shavings, with a thick and thin side, will gradually

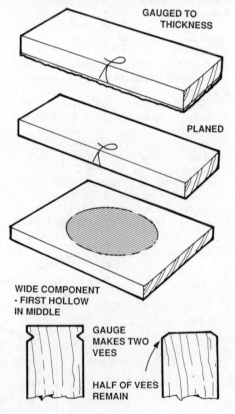

GAUGED TO THICKNESS

PLANED

WIDE COMPONENT - FIRST HOLLOW IN MIDDLE

GAUGE MAKES TWO VEES

HALF OF VEES REMAIN

Fig. 2.15

(2) Is it flat in width? (a full width shaving should make this so)
   Test with a rule in a number of places.
(3) Is it square to the face?
   Test with a try-square at intervals along the edge. The stock of the try-square must always be against the true face.
When these tests are satisfied, mark the edge ∧, the mark coinciding with the face mark α.

18

bring the edge down. Test for squareness frequently.

To finally produce to size, the required width is gauged (see page 52) from the true edge then planed to the gauge mark. It is then gauged to thickness from the true face and again planed to the gauge line. These two operations are carried out in any order.

The gauge makes a vee groove. When planing, half of this vee is removed. Removing the mark completely produces an undersized component so, if the remaining half of the gauge mark looks unsightly, ignore it as it will later be either concealed or lost in a moulding, bevel or in the final clean-up.

Planing End Grain Planing straight through the end grain produces 'spelching', that is the breaking away of the end fibres. This can be avoided by
(1) Planing to the middle from each end
(2) Chiselling off a bevel in the waste
(3) Cramping or glueing on a bevelled block.

EDGE JOINTING
The technique of planing an edge has already been described. In making an edge joint the two joining edges are prepared in this way, being straight, flat and at right angles to the true face.

Grip one board in the vice and stand the second on it, testing first, with a straight-edge, that the jointed boards will be flat, Fig. 2.17. When this has been found to be correct, push gently with an index finger on one corner. If the top board pivots, then one board is high at the pivoting spot and can be corrected (Fig. 2.18). If the top board falls off, then either the joint is correct or is hollow (Fig. 2.19). Hollowness can be seen by looking through the joint into a strong light. Nowadays when synthetic glues

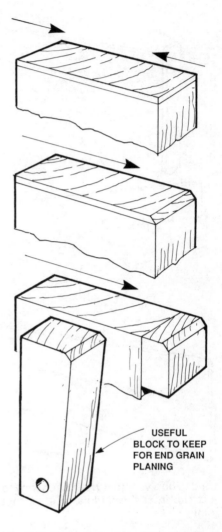

USEFUL BLOCK TO KEEP FOR END GRAIN PLANING

Fig. 2.16 Three ways of planing end grain.

have largely replaced hot scotch glue, most joints are cramped rather than rubbed. A cramped joint will permit *very* slight hollowness in the centre. The rule

19

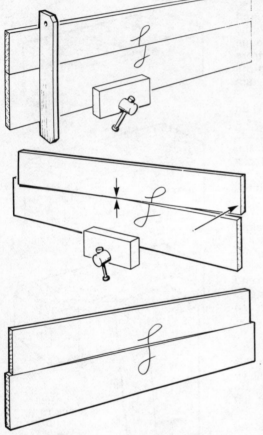

Fig. 2.17 Edge jointing test for flatness.

Fig. 2.18 Edge jointing. Pivoting will reveal high spot.

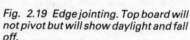

Fig. 2.19 Edge jointing. Top board will not pivot but will show daylight and fall off.

used to be a very thin worn halfpenny to just slip in at the middle of a six foot joint.

SOME OTHER PLANES

That vast collection of specialist planes which once filled so much of the space in a woodworker's tool chest is largely extinct and gone and is now of interest mainly to the collector. Most of their functions have been taken over, at least in the small workshop, by the power router or the moulding block fitted to the sawbench. A few such planes remain which in a modern form still fulfil a useful purpose, since it is often quicker in a small job to do the work by hand than it is to fit up a router with its cables, cutter and accessories.

The Rebate Plane exists in two forms. The Record 078 Duplex Rebate and

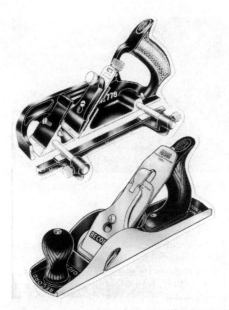

Fig. 2.20 Top, Record Duplex Rebate and Fillister, bottom Record bench rebate plane.

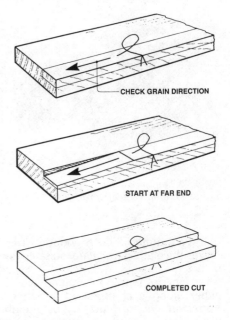

CHECK GRAIN DIRECTION

START AT FAR END

COMPLETED CUT

Fig. 2.21 Planing a rebate.

Fillister and its Stanley counterpart is a great improvement over the wooden predecessors. It has precision screw adjustment of cut. Additionally it has a fence and a spur which can be brought into use as required when working along the grain on difficult timber, or across the grain. A depth stop is also fitted.

The other version, the Record 010 and 010½ and the Stanley equivalent descends from the coachmaker's rebate plane and panel fielding planes. It is basically the jack, or smoothing, plane with its adjustments of cut, lateral and mouth with the added facility of the cutter coming through each side, which allows the cut to be made right into a corner. With a fine mouth and a close set cap iron a good finish can be obtained

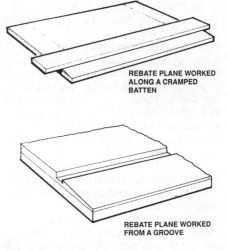

REBATE PLANE WORKED ALONG A CRAMPED BATTEN

REBATE PLANE WORKED FROM A GROOVE

Fig. 2.22 Fielding a panel.

21

Fig. 2.23 Left, shoulder planes, the Stanley pattern in the foreground and the Record behind. Right, trimming a shoulder with a shoulder plane.

on even quite difficult woods. This makes the plane particularly suitable for fielding panels.

Having no fence, this plane works either along a cramped-on batten or from a groove previously cut by plough plane, power router or circular saw.

When cutting rebates some pre-planning is necessary, particularly if using the fixed mouth planes, to make sure that the plane works along and not against the grain.

The Shoulder Plane Is in fact a special form of rebate plane. At present two forms exist – the Record and the Stanley. Designed with a low angle, especially for planing end grain, the main purpose of this plane is the planing of the shoulders of mortise and tenon joints. Narrow shoulders should, of course, fit from the saw but occasionally will require correction. Wide shoulders will always require planing. The work is generally cramped to the bench and the plane used on its side.

In addition the shoulder plane will cut small rebates. It is particularly useful on difficult woods and can be used to work small ovolo mouldings.

The Hand Router At the time of writing this is manufactured only by Stanley. Two models are available, the standard full sized model and a miniature version. In spite of the rapid development in power routing there is still a use for these tools, which can easily complete a small job before the electric router can be set up. The most common task of the router is cutting across the grain housings for shelves and partitions, often after sawcuts have been made. It conveniently cuts recesses for locks, hinges and fittings and also for inlaid features.

Though craftsmen are reluctant to admit it, occasionally tenons and bridle joints are cut over-thick. The router is by far the best tool to correct this fault. It is far more accurate than paring with a chisel. To keep the router level, an offcut of the same thickness as the job is either cramped alongside, or better still, screwed to the router sole utilising an existing hole.

These modern routers have cranked cutters, which must be kept very sharp since much of the work will be across the grain. The bevel is on top and must

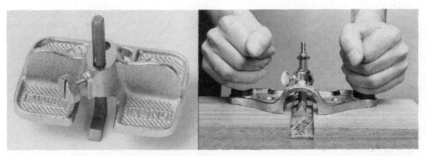

Fig. 2.24 *The Stanley miniature router is shown left and the tool in operation levelling a housing on the right.*

not be allowed to grow stubby. The sharpening, generally with a flat stone slip, follows normal methods though is rather inconvenient. The sole of the cutter, like the back of any other cutting edge, must stay dead flat with no trace of a bevel forming there.

Unavoidably, there is a certain amount of slack in the mechanism so after a cut has been completed, adjustment is made with the router standing in the cut. If it is held up in the air while the adjustment is made, as the locking collar is released, the blade will drop,

giving a greater increase in cut than was anticipated.

Unlike the rebate and plough planes, it is not feasible to fit a depth stop. A great deal of adjustment and re-adjustment can be avoided if a cut is taken from all the housings in turn, then the cut increased and all the housings given this cut, repeating until the final depth is reached.

The Plough The modern all-metal plough plane has fine screw adjustment of cut, an adjustable fence, depth stop

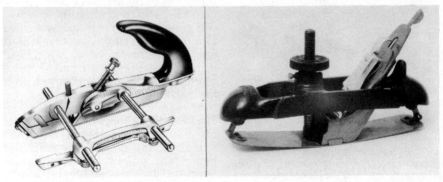

Fig. 2.25 *Left, a modern plough plane. Right, Record circular plane.*

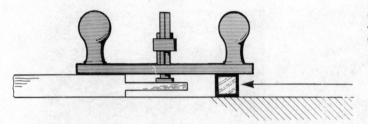

Fig. 2.26 Trueing a tenon with a hand router.

and interchangeable cutters. In addition to the standard imperial sized cutters, from ⅛ in. upwards, metric cutters are available for use with millimetre sized plywood. The small size of metal plough should not be despised. It performs well and its only limitation is the range of cutters it will accept.

Fig. 2.27 Top, low angle block plane with adjustable mouth. Above, 'three in one' plane combines functions of the shoulder, bullnose and chisel planes. Both Record.

Grooves are ploughed almost always along the grain so, again in early planning, grain direction should be observed so that wherever possible the plough cuts with the grain. The plough lacks spurs so, on difficult timber, it is recommended that the sides of the groove are first gauged with cutting gauges, set with their bevels inwards.

As with the rebate plane, short cuts are first made at the far end of the work, gradually increasing in length. Continuous pressure must be applied by the fence against the work. Unlike rebate planing where no harm is done, failure here will result in a false cut being made too close to the edge, an error which cannot be rectified.

The Compass or Circular Plane Now made only by Record, this is an extremely expensive tool for the amount of work it will produce. Its flexible sole will adjust to any required curve. It is excellent for long gentle curves which are difficult using a spokeshave. Its cost makes it more the tool of the small firm than of the individual craftsman.

The Block Plane This small single handed plane varies in type between the very crude and the precision models. The better versions with a single cutter, set bevel up at angles of 20° and 12°, are provided with cut and lateral adjustment and also a sliding mouth. These are useful planes for small jobs or details, for end grain work or for cleaning up difficult grain.

Spokeshaves These divide into two styles: the flat face, for working convex curves, and the round face, for working hollows. The metal tools are now most common, most popular and most easily obtainable. The heavier model is provided with two thumbscrews making precise adjustment easy. The lighter model with no adjustment and straight rather than cranked handles is, nevertheless, a very pleasant tool to handle, particularly on fine work. All are sharpened in the same manner as plane irons. The cutters, being small, require a simply made wooden holder for use on the oilstone or grindstone.

The older wooden spokeshaves in beech or boxwood are a pleasure to use and are still popular with many workers. After a long gap they are now on limited sale again and, of course, there are many second-hand ones about. These may require re-mouthing in ebony, rosewood or brass. Unfortunately

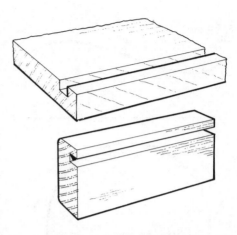

Fig. 2.28 Top, when grooving try to arrange to plane with the grain. Above, a mullet for testing the thickness of panel edges.

replacement blades are not available, so little can be done to salvage a wooden spokeshave having a well-worn blade.

Blades for wooden spokeshaves are most conveniently held in the vice while they are sharpened with a flat slipstone.

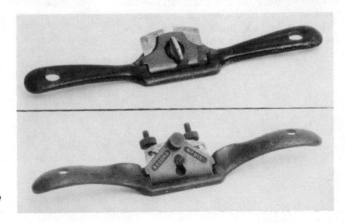

Fig. 2.29 Top, a light non-adjustable iron spokeshave, bottom an adjustable one. Both are round and flat faced.

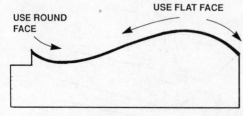

USE ROUND FACE

USE FLAT FACE

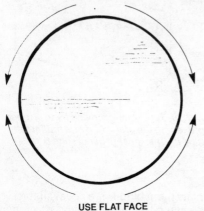

USE FLAT FACE

Fig. 2.30 Direction of cut and face used when spokeshaving.

Preserve the maker's angle on the top, not allowing it to develop too steeply. The bottom face must stay completely flat with no trace of a bevel. Adjustment

is made by light hammer taps. If the tangs have become sloppy in their holes, glue in thin slivers of wood, using the tapered tangs to cramp them in place. Later pare or file to a good working fit.

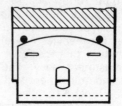

POSITIONS AND PURPOSE OF PINS

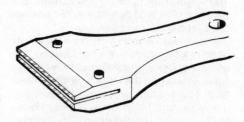

Fig. 2.31. Holder for sharpening blades from metal spokeshaves. Pins are normally tapped flush.

CHAPTER 3

SAWS AND SAWING

Saws can conveniently be divided into two groups – Ripsaws and Crosscut saws. Ripsaws are designed to cut along the grain, that is along the length of a board. Crosscuts are for cutting across the width of the board and generally for joint cutting.

These groups are distinguished by the shape of their teeth. Ripsaws have from 3 to 6 teeth per inch – 4½ is most common and 6 teeth per inch is termed Half Rip. The number of teeth is always counted inclusively. The teeth are shaped and sharpened as in Fig. 3.1. They are filed straight across, giving chisel-like teeth which remove small shavings. This saw is rapidly being replaced, where electric power is available, by small circular saws or portable jig (or sabre) saws. The family of ripsaws includes also the bowsaw, the padsaw (keyhole saw) and the coping saw. The dovetail saw (see page 29) is sharpened as a ripsaw since the bulk of its work is along the grain and the teeth are too small for crosscut sharpening.

The teeth of crosscut saws range from 4 per inch on large saws for heavy work, down to 12 teeth for panel saws and below 20 for small fine work. The teeth, shaped as in Fig. 3.2, are filed across at

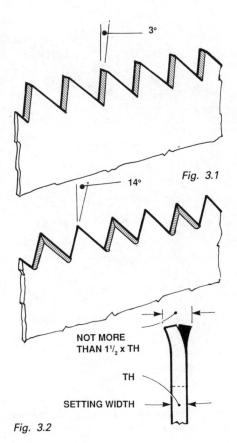

3°

14°

Fig. 3.1

NOT MORE THAN 1½ x TH

TH

SETTING WIDTH

Fig. 3.2

27

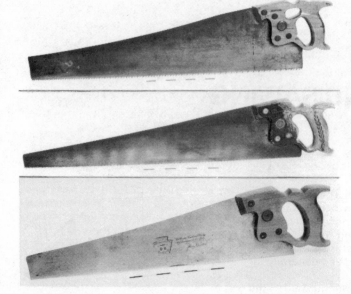

Fig. 3.3 Ripsaw. Length 28 in., 4½ teeth per inch (half rip 7 teeth per inch)

Fig. 3.4 Crosscut hand-saw. Length about 26 in., 6–8 teeth per inch.

Fig. 3.5 Panel saw. Length about 20–22 in., 10–12 teeth per inch. Note the elegant hand-grips on these tools.

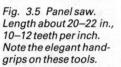

STARTING   SAWING   45°

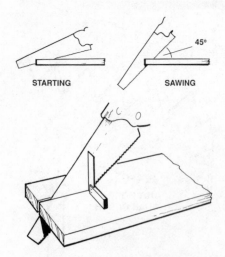

Fig. 3.6 Handsawing. Keep saw vertical and check with trysquare.

an angle, giving knife-like points which sever the fibres without splintering. At the centre of the range, rip and crosscut merge giving dual purpose saws but, at the extremes, it is not possible to sub-stitute ripping and panel saws.

USING HANDSAWS

Ripping – starting the cut Begin by drawing the blade up for several strokes, guided by the left hand thumb, which is quite safe. Remove the left hand and commence with push strokes. To begin with, keep the saw low to ensure an accurate start. Once the line has been established, raise to a convenient angle of about 45°. Check by trysquare that the saw is vertical. Handsaws are not often used on the bench, which is inconveniently high. A plank should be supported on trestles or substitutes.

Saw just clear of the gauge or pencil line to allow subsequent planing to the finished dimension.

Crosscutting The work should be similarly supported but the cut should never be made between the trestles. As such a cut nears completion, the plank will sag and the saw will stick. The offcut must overhang the trestle and be supported either by the free hand or by a helper. The subsequent start and sawing procedure is as already described.

Bench Sawing, using Backsaws It is essential that the work be well held and suported. For small pieces, a sawing board is generally sufficient. The alterna-

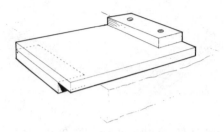

Fig. 3.7 Traditional sawing board or bench hook for a right-handed worker.

tive sawing board (Fig. 3.11) is particularly useful for small pieces and for use by beginners as it enables the workpiece to

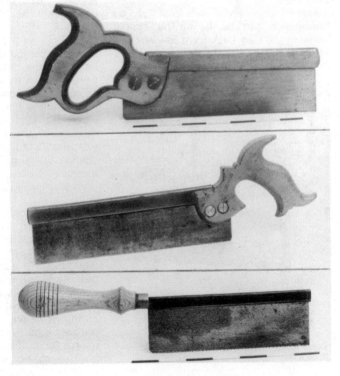

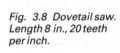

Fig. 3.8 Dovetail saw. Length 8 in., 20 teeth per inch.

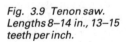

Fig. 3.9 Tenon saw. Lengths 8–14 in., 13–15 teeth per inch.

Fig. 3.10. Gents backsaw. Length 4–6 in., 20–30 teeth per inch.

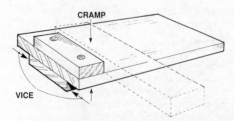

Fig. 3.11 Alternative sawing board which enables work to be held firmly with a G-cramp

be cramped. Larger work needs two sawing boards to keep it level. Important cuts are often made with the work cramped to the bench with scrap wood or hardboard beneath to protect the bench top.

Preliminary work and cuts of no importance can be begun by simply drawing the saw back for a few strokes, as with the handsaws. Important lines

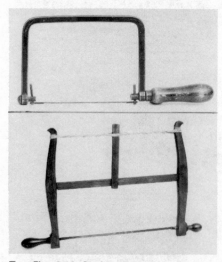

Top, Fig. 3.12 Coping saw.
Below, Fig. 3.13 Bowsaw.

should be marked with the marking knife which, unlike the pencil, has no thickness. For more precision, particularly by beginners, chisel a small notch at the far corner, in the waste, lay the saw in this, then start sawing. When making important cuts, for example wide shoulders, the knife cut should be strongly deepened and a shallow groove chiselled on the waste side. The saw is laid in this and drawn back a few times before sawing. A further alternative, particularly for very wide cuts, is to cramp a straight edged batten along the line and run the saw against this.

The Coping Saw Controversy There is endless discussion as to whether the coping saw should cut on the push or on the pull. The writer's view is that it should cut on the push like all the other saws, in particular like its relatives, the bowsaw and the metalworker's hacksaw. In this way the line can be clearly seen, unobstructed by splintering, and the action is familiar. The exception is when the coping saw is used in the manner of the fretsaw, cutting downwards on a cutting board with its vee-shaped opening. Then the teeth cut on the pull stroke, again leaving the line unobscured.

Bowsaw, Compass Saw and Padsaw (keyhole saw) The bow saw, with a narrow turning blade tensioned generally by twisted cord, cuts curves in thick wood to quite a sharp radius. The compass saw, sometimes part of a nest of saws, is virtually a short, narrow handsaw. It cuts gentle curves, not as tight as the bowsaw, very comfortably. The padsaw cuts even sharper curves. It is useful for cutting openings which the bowsaw cannot enter and which may be too sharply curved for the compass saw. It enters through a hole bored in the waste. The padsaw's hollow handle allows various lengths of the blade to be used; for example, a shorter blade for very sharp curves. The small electric jigsaw has mainly ousted these saws.

Sawing Tenons This routine task is obviously done with the tenon saw. Since the work is along the grain and is in effect through a considerable thickness, the reader is strongly advised to have a tenon saw re-cut with ripsaw teeth of about 9 or 10 per inch. This ensures a fast easy cut. The longer the saw operates in the sawcut, the greater is the danger of wandering off.

The tenons should have been carefully marked out using a mortise gauge and marking knife. Do not attempt to saw down more than one line at a time and do not saw down a line which is out of sight.

Start at the further corner, slowly lowering the saw until a cut has been made right along the end grain, of about ⅛ in. depth. The component is then tilted in the vice and the nearside gauge line sawn to. The saw never comes out of the initial sawcut, but no attempt is made to saw to the line which is out of sight. The work or the worker is reversed and the process repeated, leaving a small triangle in the centre. The job is then returned to the vertical and the saw run down the existing cuts. Any set in or haunch is sawn next.

Finally the shoulders are sawn off, for accuracy, using the chiselled groove method described. Take the greatest care not to saw too deep and into the

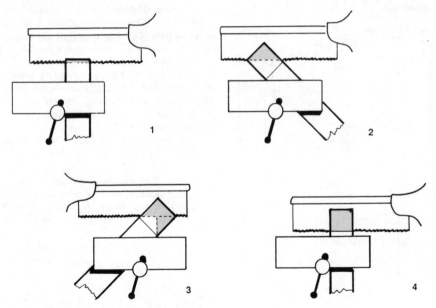

Fig. 3.14 Stages in sawing tenon cheeks.

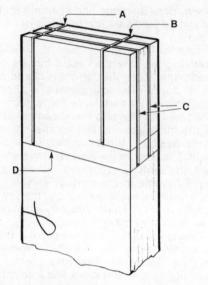

Fig. 3.15 Sawing a tenon (ready for the shoulder cuts).

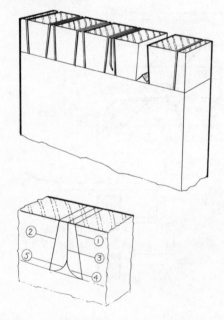

Left, Fig. 3.16 Removal of waste from a common dovetail with a coping saw. Note stages of sawing. Below, Fig. 3.17. The same saw used to remove waste from a lap dovetail.

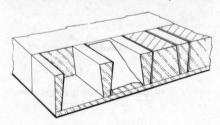

tenon. If, having sawn to depth, the cheek does not fall off, then the vertical cut has stopped short. In this case, insert a chisel to snap off the cheek then clean up.

Sawing Dovetails This is very precise work and great accuracy is required. This is not achieved by sawing wide and chiselling back to the mark. Practice and confidence are needed to saw up to but not across the line. A dovetail saw is not necessarily essential. This fine saw is needed for small dovetails. Larger ones are quite successfully sawn with a sharp tenon saw. Once having had to sharpen a dovetail saw, the reader will be most economical with its use thereafter.

The Common (or through) Dovetail. The tails are generally sawn first. Some workers find it a help to tilt the work so as to saw vertically. Having sawn the tails, the waste was formerly chiselled out. Nowadays, the bulk is sawn with the coping saw. Turning a coping saw blade at the bottom of the tenon saw cut can bruise the dovetail at its corner. The waste is then better removed by sawing from the centre as indicated. The remaining waste is removed by chisel. The sockets in the other half of the joint are similarly removed.

The Drawer or Lap Dovetail. The tails are cut in the way just described. In

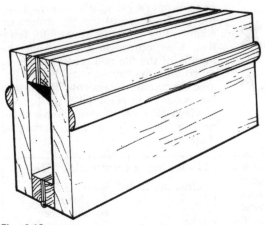

Fig. 3.18

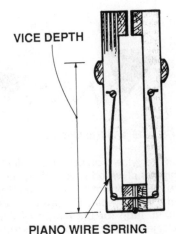

VICE DEPTH

PIANO WIRE SPRING

making the sockets, the tenon saw makes a diagonal cut, then an appreciable amount of waste is sawn out with the coping saw. A chisel completes the job.

SHARPENING SAWS

Saws which need sharpening generally fall into one of four categories: the new saw that has not previously been resharpened; the well-maintained saw; the poorly-sharpened saw; and the saw with broken teeth.

Each of these needs its own special treatment, though some processes are common to all. Most steps will be covered by considering a saw which has previously been poorly sharpened.

There are two main families of saw, the ripping saws and the crosscutting saws. The former consists of the ripsaw, the half ripsaw, the dovetail saw, bowsaw, padsaw, coping saw and, as described later, the rip/tenon saw. Crosscuts include the handsaw, panel saw and tenon saw.

The ripsaw family is filed across at right angles to give teeth like small chisels (Fig. 3.1). You can see the cutting action if you use a ⅛ in. chisel to simulate one tooth; along the grain you can cut a clean groove rapidly and easily; working across the grain produces a poor groove with very splintered sides.

The crosscuts are filed at an angle, giving teeth like little knives (Fig. 3.2). To simulate this action, two heavy knife lines must be made across the grain and the waste chipped out with something smaller and less efficient than the ⅛ in. chisel.

The practical effect is that the ripsaw cuts easily, quickly and cleanly along the grain but makes a rough job with rather hard work across the grain. On the other hand, the crosscut cuts quickly, smoothly and easily across the grain but while it will produce a clean cut along the grain it is slower and harder work.

Saw Vice You need a saw vice before you can start work on a saw. As this is quite expensive and will be used infrequently by the amateur and small business craftsman, it is suggested that the model illustrated (Fig. 3.18) or something like it, is made.

33

Fig. 3.19 Width of file face.

The vice consists basically of two hinged plywood jaws with spacing strips top and bottom to accept the thickness of a saw handle. The jaws can be about 10 in. long (or the length of the bench vicejaws) with two rounded strips on the outside to take the pressure of the bench vice. The inside capacity of the saw vice should be such that the widest handsaw will fit in. A smaller vice simply for tenon saws may be made. Line the jaws with leather or rubber (pieces from an old car inner tube are quite suitable) to reduce the unpleasant noise often associated with saw sharpening. One end of the saw vice jaws may need cutting away to accept the handles of small saws. An opening spring made from piano wire is a convenience.

Files The first file needed is a 10 in. second cut mill file. This shouldn't be used for rough work; keep it carefully stored in a plastic sleeve or cloth (it can be used to sharpen scrapers and scraper plane blades).

Choose the triangular files with care, for their life, when used on the best

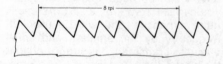

Fig. 3.20 Teeth are counted inclusively.

saws, is not very long. It's important that the working face of the file should be slightly over twice the saw tooth depth (Fig. 3.19), otherwise a strip down the middle of the file will receive twice as much wear as the corners. Points per inch are counted inclusively. Too large a file creates too rounded a gullet. Roll sawfiles in a cloth; don't leave them rattling about in a box damaging themselves.

Choosing a triangular file	
Points per inch	**Suitable File**
4½, 5, 6,	7in slim taper
7, 8,	6in slim taper
9, 10,	5in or 5½in slim taper
11, 12, 13, 14, 15,	4½in slim taper
over 16,	4in extra slim taper
extra fine saws	needle file
4, 5 and 6in files are available as regular taper, slim taper and extra slim taper.	

For poor eyesight, or working under poor lighting conditions, it is recommended engineer's blue marking fluid be used to show which teeth have been filed. Those old reading spectacles come in handy for fine saws, worn on the top of the others; they magnify well but one does have to come rather close. Commercial clip-on magnifiers are available at a price.

A saw which has been poorly sharpened in the past requires four operations:
(1) Topping (sometimes called jointing)
(2) Shaping
(3) Setting
(4) Sharpening.

Topping The teeth may be of different heights or the edge may have been sharpened hollow (or round) or both. Fix the saw in the vice, hold a mill file (without its handle) along the blade and square to it, then run it along the length of the saw. Rocking the file, since this will round over the teeth, can be prevented by holding the file in a grooved block (Fig. 3.21); for this the saw must be raised well above the vice jaws.

Topping produces a 'shiner' on the top of each tooth (Fig. 3.22); make sure that each tooth has one (a wipe of the blue marking fluid is helpful here).

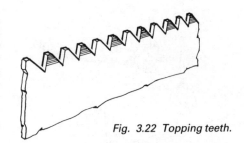

Fig. 3.22 Topping teeth.

Shaping Select an appropriate triangular file, and hold it horizontally at right angles to the saw, and twisted to an angle of 14° to the vertical for crosscut saws and 3° for ripsaws (Fig. 3.23). Some people prefer less than 14° but the angle should be substantial. These are the theoretical angles and individual saws may have been cut slightly differently; the angle

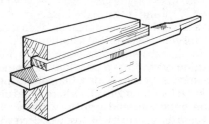

Fig. 3.21 Fitting a file in a grooved block to prevent rocking.

can be found from the unused teeth by the handle.

File half of a shiner with the file in one gullet, then the remainder with the file in the next. Once these shiners are filed away, top again until every tooth gets a shiner; this method prevents the spacing being lost and ensures teeth of equal height. A useful aid is a part-used sawfile which has had the teeth ground off one side (Fig. 3.24); this permits a bad tooth

to be filed without danger to a good one.

It's not particularly difficult to keep the 90° angle constant but retaining the angle of 3° or 14° is; the wrist gets quickly tired by rigidly holding that angle and of course if work is interrupted it is difficult to pick up exactly the angle again.

There are devices which may help. There is a commercial British saw filer which appears attractive and works well, but requires special tangless files which are not commonly stocked; also the file is large, thus making work on fine tenon saws impossible.

Alternatively you can make the device shown in Fig. 3.25. Turn or whittle a decent handle and fit it with a tight metal ferrule. Make a second ferrule to fit over this and rotate. Solder a threaded nut or block to this outer ferrule and continue

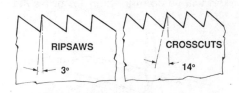

RIPSAWS   3°

CROSSCUTS   14°

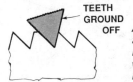

TEETH GROUND OFF

Above, Fig. 3.23 Shaping teeth.
Left, Fig. 3.24 A file with one face ground is helpful.

35

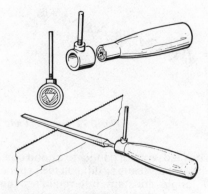

Fig. 3.25. A simple angle guide.

the thread through. A 4 in. rod with a screwdriver slot screws into this and clamps on the inner ferrule. To use, settle the file firmly in a good gullet, swing the rod horizontal or vertical according to preference and lock there. It will be found much easier to maintain the angle using this rod as a guide or sight.

Shaping is complete when all the teeth have lost their shiners and the gullets are all the same depth.

Setting Teeth are bent to alternate sides, so that the saw doesn't bind in the kerf. Setting should be arranged so that the kerf will be no more than 1½ times the

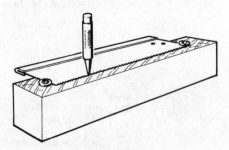

Fig. 3.26 Setting very fine teeth.

sawblade thickness. Softwoods require greater set than hardwoods and wet wood more still. Taper-ground handsaws require very little set. It is vital that each tooth be given exactly the same set; if not the saw will want to run out of line, a fault often incorrectly attributed to teeth not holding their edge. Only the top half of a tooth should be set. Never attempt to reset teeth to the opposite side: this will cause cracking and loss of teeth, as will trying to bend over the whole tooth. The most common fault in home maintained saws is oversetting.

The pliers-type sawset offers the best setting method to the amateur. Several patterns are on the market but examine them carefully before buying. One make will cope with only below 12 teeth per inch; another can be dismantled and filed to do smaller work. The Stanley 42SS, made in the USA, sets between 4 and 16 tpi and is one of the best currently available. The Disston No. 28 does 4 to 10 tpi while the No. 280 sets 10 to 16 tpi.

In the absence of a sawset, or for setting very fine teeth, the following method is recommended. Carefully plane a short length of 2 in. thick hardwood on one endgrain, and grip it in the vice. Secure the saw to it with two woodscrews and large washers. The set is put on alternate teeth using a fine punch, preferably brass, giving two or three light blows with a small hammer. The saw is turned over and the process repeated.

After setting, place the saw flat on the bench and lightly run an oilstone along the teeth; turn over and repeat. This corrects the odd tooth which may be too prominent, thus preventing a jump when sawing.

Sharpening Different methods are used for sharpening saws of the ripsaw and crosscut families.

Ripsaws are sharpened at 90°, in the same manner as the teeth were reshaped. Fix the saw in the vice with the handle to the right. Top the saw again, very lightly putting a small shiner on each tooth. Now blue the teeth. File at right angles to the saw and horizontal, starting on the front edge of the first tooth set towards you and continue on alternate teeth (Fig. 3.27). Two or three steady push strokes should be enough to take off half of the shiner. It's the front edge of the tooth towards you that gets the filing; this puts any 'rag' or roughness on the tooth to the inside, where it has no effect and is lost in work. The blueing helps, particularly with small saws, to make sure that two adjacent teeth are not filed. At the end, reverse the saw and sawvice also if preferred (handle now on the left) and continue to file the front edge of the tooth set towards you. Do not save time by filing every tooth at 90° from the same side: it makes the saw run to one side.

Crosscut saws are sharpened at an angle, not at 90°, giving bevelled teeth producing knife-like edges. A long, thin bevel on a tooth (Fig. 3.28) cuts well for a time, particularly on dry hardwoods, but quickly wears, so a shorter bevel is more suitable for general use.

Again fix the saw in the vice, projecting about ¼ in. with the handle at the right and lightly top all the teeth. Blue them at this stage. Begin filing on the front edge of the first tooth set towards you (Fig. 3.29). The file handle is moved to the left to make an angle of 65° to 75° depending on preference and the type of timber expected to be worked: softwoods take a thinner bevel, hardwoods a stouter one. Maintain this angle, filing alternate teeth and removing half of the shiner. It may be found helpful to mark this angle in pencil on the top of the saw vice jaws. On reaching the end, reverse

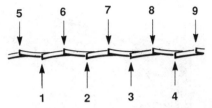

Fig. 3.27 Ripsaw sharpening order of strokes.

the saw (handle to left) and repeat, removing the remaining half of the shiner, keeping the file horizontal at all times.

Angles If experienced, then angles become a matter of personal preference. The angles stated are about 14° front angle for a crosscut saw and about 3° for a rip. These are the angles which Spear & Jackson say they put on their saws; their tenon saw, being a crosscut, is given 16°. Disstons claim to put on 15° for a crosscut saw and 8° for a ripsaw. When the angle to the front of the tooth is appreciably more than recommended it is described as having too much 'hook' or pitch and may 'hang up' or jolt

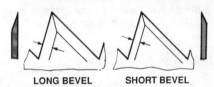

LONG BEVEL   SHORT BEVEL

Fig. 3.28 Crosscut sharpening.

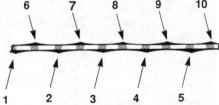

Fig. 3.29 Order of file strokes, crosscut.

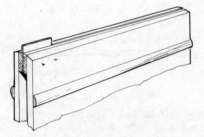

Fig. 3.30 A piece of metal pinned in the vice jaws provides a guide at the saw's end.

suddenly in the cut which could cause a kink in the blade.

Fine dovetail saws have such small teeth that if filed front and back at say 70°, there would be no tooth left. So sharpen them with a needle file at 90° as a ripsaw. As most of their work is with the grain this is no disadvantage.

Rip tenon saws For sawing through a 2½ in. board one would use a ripsaw of probably 4½ tpi, the saw built for the job. For sawing the cheeks of a 2½ in. wide tenon, most workers use a tenon saw of 15 tpi whose teeth have been specifically filed for crosscutting. This really doesn't make sense so the making of a rip tenon saw is a suggestion.

Obtain a second tenon saw with sufficient depth of blade left to cope with the average tenon. Also needed is an old power hacksaw blade of 9 or 10 tpi. With the mill file, file off the teeth from the tenon blade. Cramp the hacksaw blade and the tenon saw together in the saw vice and, using the hacksaw blade as a guide, file the new teeth until the hacksaw blade stops further filing; this is a bit rough on the file but it only happens once. Having got the teeth well marked proceed exactly as for topping and shaping; then set and sharpen. This saw will cut tenons more accurately and rapidly than the standard crosscut tenon saw, for the longer the saw runs in the kerf the easier it is to get off line.

Broken teeth When one or more teeth are completely missing there is quite a lengthy job. Top the saw strongly giving quite large shiners. Then shape, bringing the teeth to points. Give a touch to the gullets on each side of the broken tooth so that they remain the same depth as the others. Continue topping and shaping for a number of times until the new teeth emerge and are the same height as the others. The standard routine is then followed.

Fig. 3.31. Recutting the teeth to make a rip-tenon saw.

38

New saws Well maintained and new saws require the minimum of topping, just sufficient to reveal that no tooth has been damaged by perhaps being caught on some metal. If all is well the shaping process may be omitted for a few treatments and the sharpening proceeded with right away. Few people appreciate how little set is required, so frequently two or three light sharpenings can be carried out without resetting. A little and often can be regarded as a sound maxim for saw care.

Maintenance A sharp saw should be well protected when not in use. Either hang it up or use a teeth guard as in Fig. 3.32, held in place with two strong rubber bands. Most damage occurs to saws left lying in the well of the bench where they meet cramps, hammers and other metal agents.

The blade should be kept very lightly oiled. A carpet oil pad (a rectangle of

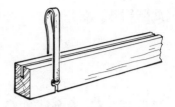

Fig. 3.32 Protecting a saw.

carpet glued to a wooden block) is the most convenient way to do this.

The requirements for good saw sharpening are therefore:
(1) Sharp files
(2) A firm vice
(3) Good lighting
(4) Good eyesight (or good spectacles)
(5) Plenty of time
(6) And don't talk or, if possible, don't allow interruptions.

CHAPTER 4

CHISELS AND GOUGES

Of the many varieties of chisel, five are in common use so only these will be considered.

The Firmer Chisel This is a fairly robust chisel for general bench work. It will

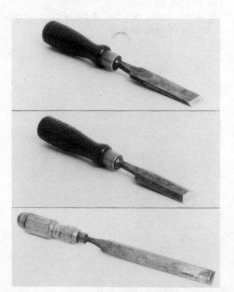

Figs. 4.1, 4.2 and 4.3 show, top to bottom, firmer, bevel-edged firmer and long, thin bevel-edged paring chisel.

stand up to quite heavy chopping. Like most chisels it generally has a shouldered tang. The alternative form is the socket type in which the handle goes into the chisel.

The Bevel Edge Chisel This has a lighter, thinner blade, built generally for paring though it will stand light malleting. It is the essential tool for chopping dovetails as Fig. 4.7 makes clear. When buying a bevel edge chisel examine the edges (sides) carefully. Many modern ones are excessively thick here which is a distinct disadvantage when dovetailing. Old bevel edge chisels were beautifully thin here.

The Paring Chisel These are extra long (often with 10 in. blades), extra thin, bevel edge chisels built specifically for fine paring and should not be struck.

The Mortise Chisel This is designed, as the name implies, specifically for chopping mortises. Its thickness is considerably greater than its width (ie its size). The handle is massive, generally of beech. Its oval section is intended to give a good grip to avoid twisting in the mortise. The shoulder or flange is very

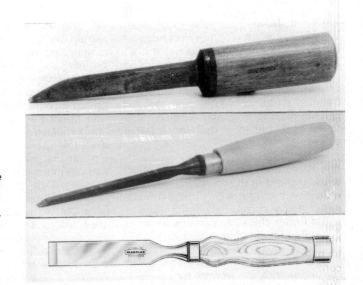

Fig. 4.4 The true mortise chisel

Fig. 4.5 Sash mortise chisels, also known as the London or cabinet Pattern mortise chisel.

Fig. 4.6 The 'registered' chisel.

large and has a leather shock-absorbing washer between it and the handle. Though much mortising is now done by machine, this is still a useful tool to have for other than very light work, since its great thickness enables it to stand up to the levering out of the waste, a task which accounts for many broken, lighter chisels.

The Sash Mortise Chisel This is a lighter version of the mortise chisel originally

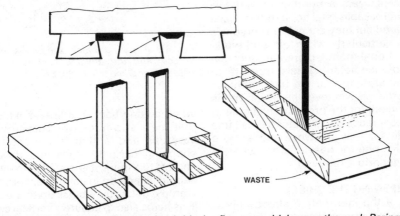

WASTE

Fig. 4.7 Dovetails require a bevel-edged chisel: a firmer would damage the work. Paring into a waste block (right) prevents break-out of the far edge.

designed for the mortising of sash window frames. It is sometimes referred to as the London Pattern. It has a finer handle, often boxwood, still retaining the leather washer, and is considerably thicker than a firmer chisel of the same nominal width. It is the ideal tool for cabinet-making tasks and is much more freely available than the true mortise chisel.

The Registered Chisel This tool, often found jostling in the toolbag of jobbing workmen, has little to commend it. It is a rather heavy chisel, between a mortise and a firmer chisel. A leather washer is generally fitted while the top of the handle is given an iron band. This is to prevent splitting when used, as in common, with a hammer by itinerant workmen. If a mallet is used, it is soon damaged. When chopping mortises, this tool is more likely to twist than a true mortise chisel.

Handles were formerly of the carver, bottle or octagon forms, in ash, beech or for the better chisels, boxwood. The octagon handles were invariably of box. In recent years a number of varieties of unbreakable plastic handles have appeared but they are not to everyone's taste, particularly when old and work-worn. Some manufacturers fit only one size of handle to chisels from ⅛ to 1½ in., arguing that the hand remains the same size whatever the chisel. This is convenient for the production engineer, but most readers will prefer a small fine handle for delicate work and a more massive one for heavier work where a stronger grip is required.

SHARPENING THE CHISEL
Most of the information already given on sharpening applies to chisels. The normal grinding angle should be between 20° and 25° while the honing angle should be between that and 30°. The long thin paring chisel will have a smaller grinding angle while the mortise chisel will be slightly greater. On this tool, the honing angle should be kept close to the grinding angle for best results.

In direct paring, the flat side of the blade slides over the cut surface. Paring with the grain gives success. Paring against the grain is impossible as the work splinters ahead of the cutting edge. Any trace of bevel on the flat side produces a tool which will no longer pare. As with planing, chiselling end grain will cause bursting out, or spelching, on the far corner so this operation, to be successful, must be carried out on a smooth-faced block of waste wood. When a sizeable end grain cut is being made, the strength of the shaving will minutely force the chisel backwards so,

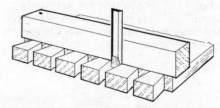

Fig. 4.8 A paring block keeps the chisel vertical and the dovetail sockets in line. Glasspaper glued to the block helps.

when cutting back to a line, make sure that the last one or two shavings are very thin and lacking this strength. In chopping back dovetails and dovetail sockets to a mark, it is essential that they should all end up in line. To ensure this, cramp a thick guide block up to the line. This helps also to ensure a vertical cut. A strip of glasspaper cut just narrower than the block, glued beneath, prevents

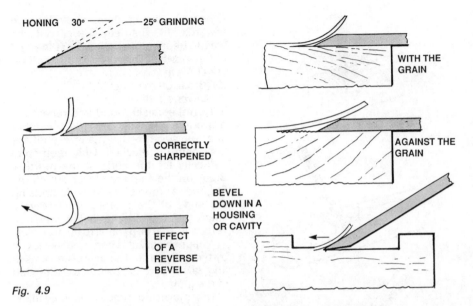

HONING   30°   25° GRINDING

CORRECTLY
SHARPENED

EFFECT
OF A
REVERSE
BEVEL

WITH THE
GRAIN

AGAINST THE
GRAIN

BEVEL
DOWN IN A
HOUSING
OR CAVITY

Fig. 4.9

slipping when applying the cramps.

The honing bevel must not be allowed to grow too big as this impairs performance. Generally, softer woods can take a thinner bevel than harder woods. Too thin a bevel used on end grain is liable to crumble or break.

When a fair amount of chiselling is to be undertaken the leather strop should be kept at hand and frequently used.

CHOPPING A MORTISE

For a start, do not mortise in the vice if avoidable. Cramp the work securely either to the bench top or, better still, to a mortising block held in the vice. If the work must be gripped in the vice, have below it a slightly thinner packing piece resting on the vice bars. This will prevent the work sliding downwards during the process and becoming scored.

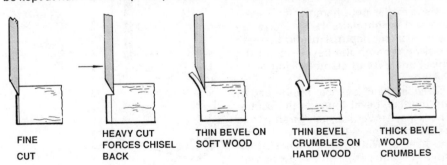

FINE
CUT

HEAVY CUT
FORCES CHISEL
BACK

THIN BEVEL ON
SOFT WOOD

THIN BEVEL
CRUMBLES ON
HARD WOOD

THICK BEVEL
WOOD
CRUMBLES

Fig. 4.10

43

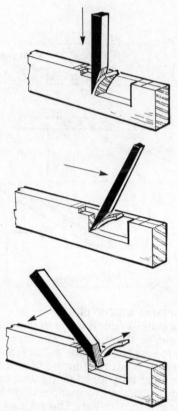

Fig. 4.11 Mortising sequence-drive in, break off, then lever out.

the chip by pushing the handle forward towards the first cut. Lever out the waste. Repeat this until almost the end of the mortise. This, then, is the routine:

(1) Drive in
(2) Break off the chip
(3) Lever out the waste.

Turn the chisel round and repeat the procedure, moving towards the other end. Carry on in this manner until the final depth is reached. Only then chop vertically for the ends of the mortise. Break off the chip then lever out on the finger or a wood block to avoid bruising the ends of the mortise. At intervals, check that the chisel is being driven in vertically, that is, parallel to the true face.

A haunch socket is generally removed by two very careful sawcuts then chiselling, taking care to observe the direction of the grain.

The mortising process is fully illustrated (see Figs. 4.11–14) and this procedure must be followed. Do not twist the chisel, do not let it move sideways in the manner of a car gear lever and, above all, do not pare down the sides of the cavity. As the whole mortising

Use a mallet, not a hammer, and pick a size and weight suitable for the job in hand. Mark the depth of the mortise with masking tape on the bevel face of the chisel only. Try to stand looking along the mortise.

Drive in the chisel near the far end of the mortise, bevel towards the centre. Check that it is vertical, using a short rule or straight-edge. A long one will foul on the handle. Withdraw the chisel, then drive in again, perhaps ⅛ in. away, with the bevel facing the first cut. Break off

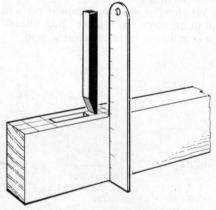

Fig. 4.12 Checking that the chisel is vertical.

system is geared to the width of the chisel to be used, any of these irregularities can only make the mortise oversize. Inside a mortise, accuracy is the requirement, not a fine finish.

When a pair of mortises is being cut, as for a table or stool leg, if the first mortise is chopped to its finished depth, then the second will be chopped over a cavity, resulting frequently in the inside corner breaking off. This can be avoided. Mark the first and second depth on the masking tape. The first mortise is chopped short of the finished depth. The second mortise, cut to finished depth, meets the first one without breaking out. Where necessary the internal corner can be trimmed square with a broad chisel.

A useful addition to the range of standard chisels is a pair of dovetailing chisels. ¼ in. (6 mm) is the most convenient size. Bevelled edges are not essential. These chisels are ground to about 10° or 12° then honed in the normal way. The corners of the sockets for lap or drawer dovetails are most efficiently cleaned up up using these chisels.

The cutting of housings and halvings is clearly shown in Figs. 4.16–19. When dovetailing, chop from both sides and with a small straight-edge or the side of the chisel, test for flatness in the gap. A hump here will push the other component forward, out of shape. The

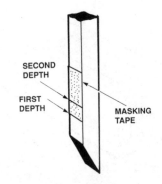

Fig. 4.14 Marking cut depth

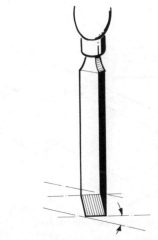

Fig. 4.15 Dovetailing chisel, about ¼ in., with cutting edge angled at 10–12°.

smallest amount of hollowness will not materially affect the joint, but such hollow sockets must certainly not be aimed at. Dovetailing in softer timbers calls for a longer, thinner bevel and keener edge to prevent crumbling at the centre.

OLD CHISELS
These are probably the most common old tools. A split handle can easily be

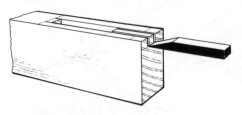

Fig. 4.13 Making the haunch socket.

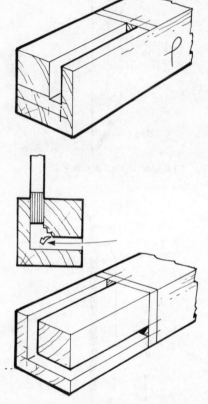

Fig. 4.16 Cutting a pair of mortises.

replaced. Those blobs of hardened paint and putty can be got rid of. A chipped and broken edge can be ground back into use. But examine the flat face carefully. If this is pitted with rust, the tool will be of little use. With grinding and honing, some rust pits will eventually appear as small chips in the cutting edge.

GOUGES

For general bench work, as distinct from carving, there are basically two gouges. Firmer gouges are ground on the outside and the scribing gouge on the inside.

The firmer gouge is for general bench work, for example making shallow recesses for finger grips. It is sharpened on an oilstone, like a chisel, but with a constant rolling motion. Roll sufficiently to ensure that the corners also are sharpened, not just the middle. Firmer gouges are generally ground to a slight curve. The burr on the inside is removed with a slipstone of the same or slightly smaller radius than the gouge.

The scribing gouge can be compared with the paring chisel. In fact in its longer thinner form it is generally referred to as a paring gouge, hence it is absolutely essential that the flat side of the tool remain so. The inside bevel is sharpened

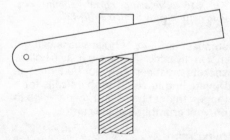

Fig. 4.17 Check when chopping dove-tails that the cut is flat.

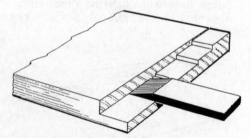

Fig. 4.18 Chisel removes bulk of waste in end-grain rebate. Watch grain direction!

Fig. 4.19 Bulk of housing waste removed by chisel, bevel down. Finish with hand router.

Fig. 4.20 Removing bulk of waste in a cross-halving after weakening by sawcuts.

with a slipstone as close as possible to its own radius. The burr is removed on the oilstone holding the gouge quite flat and rotating back and forth. In view of the difficulty in getting this gouge ground (special grinding facilities are required), it is wise to spend that extra time honing on the grinding bevel, thus putting off regrinding as long as possible. The main use of this gouge is for scribing the sockets or cavities to match mouldings, work now generally done by machine or router. This tool has considerable use by pattern makers.

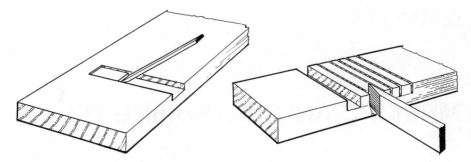

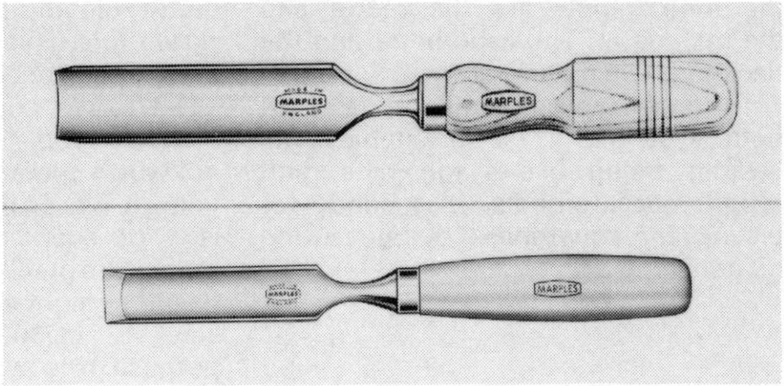

Fig. 4.21 Firmer gouge, ground externally.

Fig. 4.22 Scribing gouge, ground internally.

47

CHAPTER 5

MARKING AND MEASURING TOOLS

Like it or not, the worker in the English-speaking world will have to resign himself to the fact that the metric system has come to stay. This means that, whatever the personal preference, the worker must be equipped for measuring in both imperial and in metric units. As far as woodworkers are concerned, the metric units are the metre and the millimetre. The centimetre and the decimeter are not used.

The steel tape generally copes with both systems. It is pocketable and, besides being useful for initial and rough measurements, it is handy for testing for squareness by measuring diagonals.

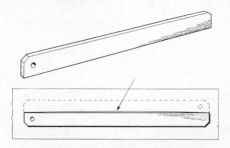

Fig. 5.1 Wooden straight-edge, useful in various sizes. Arrowed gap reveals error.

Folding rules, for a long time the most popular with woodworkers, are not very often scaled in both units. The small, neat, 2 ft. four fold has always been the preference of the cabinet maker while the bigger work of the joiner and carpenter has led to them choosing the 3 ft. Metric has brought in the four fold metre rule and the Continental six fold zigzag rule. This latter fits conveniently into pockets but lacks rigidity.

A 3 ft. or 1 m rigid rule is always useful in a workshop, hung near the bench. It is not worth spending a great deal on this item. A 2ft. or 600 mm rigid steel rule is worth spending more on. The calibrations are precise and it serves also as a useful straight-edge. On the bench the steel 12 in./300 mm is the general purpose rule while the 6 in./150 mm is handy in the overall pocket. These two are the most convenient to which gauges and fences are set. Spend a little extra on the stainless or 'rustless chrome' models which stay legible for a lifetime.

A steel straight-edge is quite an expensive item in which not many woodworkers will feel the need to invest. An assortment of wooden straight-edges can be built up as required. Make these from very old seasoned wood, preferably taken from old furniture. Plane true on a freshly sharpened planer. Drill a hanging hole, since storing hung helps to prevent bowing. Test for straightness by drawing a line full length, then turning end over end and repeating. Any error will be apparent.

Next in importance to straightness comes the right-angle, which is tested with the try-square. Three are required, though a fourth, a small engineer's 2 in. or 3 in. square is useful for dovetailing and small work. The 6 in. (150 mm) and 12 in. (300 mm) are the most useful sizes for bench work. My preference is for the all-metal models which generally keep their accuracy better.

For marking out large plywood and similar sheets, an all-wood model is useful. This can easily be built up from layers of ¼ in. (6 mm) ply. Use best quality beech ply if possible and avoid the 'Stoutheart' with its thin-skinned thick-centre layer. Test by applying the 3.4.5 rule of Pythagoras.

The wood square must not be used with the marking knife. The metal squares suffer two types of damage. Frequent dropping will knock them out of square. To test this, plane or machine a straight edge and with a sharp hard pencil, square a line. Turn over the square and repeat. Any error will be obvious. Refrain from filing true, since both edges of the blade will require treatment and must end up truly parallel. Instead, with a wood block, try to knock it back, then perhaps tap the rivets a bit tighter.

After a lot of use with the marking knife, particularly in a communal workshop, the outer edge of the blade becomes worn. Here the only remedy is careful filing with frequent testing.

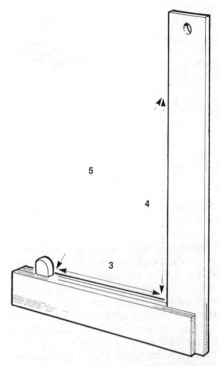

Fig. 5.2 Large wooden try-square – make 3ft. or 4ft. Check by 3,4,5 rule.

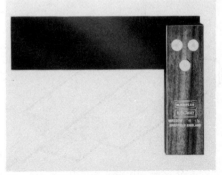

Fig. 5.3 Conventional try-square.

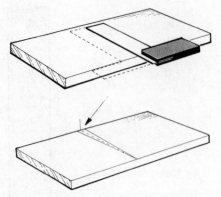

Fig. 5.4 Testing a try-square. Error revealed as arrowed.

Sliding bevels are necessary for angles other than right angles. Some are tightened with a clamping lever which is more convenient than having to fetch a screwdriver. Every care must be taken that the bevel is not knocked or dropped during the job. The bevel can often be dispensed with by using a taper block between the work and a try-square. If the block is preserved, the precise angle can be re-used later in the job or for a correction.

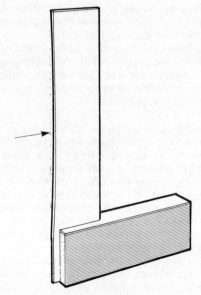

Fig. 5.5. Try-square showing wear after considerable use with marking knife.

The mitre square is notorious for becoming untrue. Unless a great deal of mitring is to be undertaken it is doubtful whether it is worth buying. A simplified engineer's combination set, manufac-

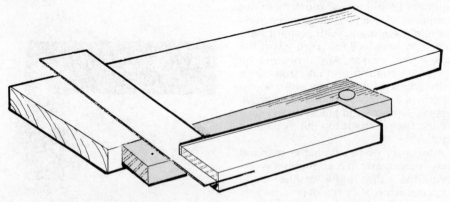

Fig. 5.6 Marking an angle by means of an interposed tapered block.

tured to a lower quality, has found its way into many tool boxes and this gives a passable 45°.

Draughtsman's set squares, 45° and 30°/60° in largish sizes and without thin bevelled edges prove useful for checking interior angles and for accurately setting the sliding bevel. Being made of one piece they do not lose their accuracy.

Pencils are worth a mention. Apart from an HB for general workshop scribbling, others are useful. A very soft pencil is required, which will not dent the wood, for marking faces and edges, identifying joints and general instructions such as top, back, inside. The traditional flat woodworker's pencil in the soft grade cannot be bettered. An alternative is a 4B or 6B. Many glue-ups have gone wrong due to confusion caused by spidery lettering with hard pencils. This tends to happen when working at speed with several helpers.

For fine, critical marking, for example dovetails, a 2H or 4H is required. If the wood does not not take this well, give a wipe with shellac sanding sealer. This roughens the surface slightly, giving a key for the pencil.

There is a lot of hostility to the use of the ballpoint on wood. However, it has the merits of clarity and even thickness. The fine ballpoint is to be preferred.

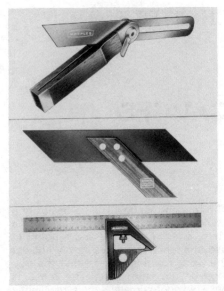

Figs. 5.7, 8 and 9; top to bottom, the sliding bevel, the mitre square and the combination square.

However, think first whether the area will later be skimmed over, removing the indelible marks. If not, do not use.

There is no need to cut away wood to remove unwanted pencil marks. The rather coarse ink or typewriting eraser does the job well.

CHAPTER 6

GAUGES

The Marking Gauge This is basically a marker of parallel lines. It consists of a stem, a fence, a screw and a point. In use, the fence is pushed firmly against the work, running along either the true face or the true edge. The fence is adjusted approximately, the screw lightly tightened then the final adjustment is made by gently tapping the appropriate end of the stem on the bench top. The screw is then fully tightened. Looking from the point end, right-handed workers will prefer the screw on the left and left-handers on the right.

When gauging, the point should not be stabbed in vertically but should trail along the wood. The gauge runs on a corner of the stem, which is rotated in the hand to increase or decrease the depth of the marking.

It is an advantage, particularly for a beginner, if the stem is drilled at a slight angle so as to facilitate this trailing action. Drill appropriately for left or right handed use. The point should be kept really sharp and should not project greatly. 1/16 in. (2 mm) is quite enough. Gauges are often found in school or communal workshops which have points projecting as much as 1/4 in. (6 mm). This is a disadvantage and does not lead to a clean, crisp gauge line.

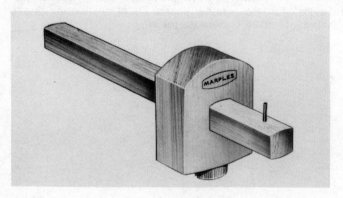

Fig. 6.1 The marking gauge.

Fig. 6.2 Using the marking gauge.

Fig. 6.3 Gauging a small piece in the vice: the start of the stroke.

Fig. 6.4 The end of the stroke. Note that the workpiece has been moved through the vice.

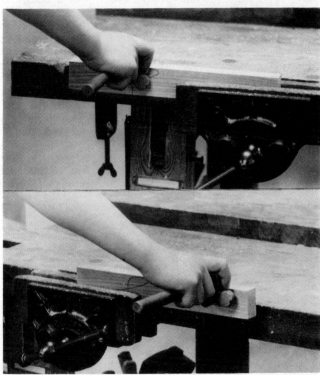

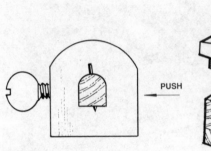

Fig. 6.5 Right-handed gauge with trailing pointer.

PUSH

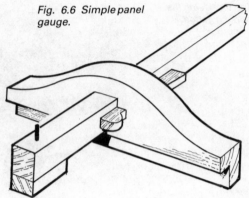

Fig. 6.6 Simple panel gauge.

A reminder. When planing to a gauge mark, continue until half of the vee-shaped groove has been removed.

The marking gauge operates along the grain. If it is used across the grain, the fibres are torn.

For early, rough marking-out it is convenient to use a pencil gauge, fitted with a pencil or a ball-point or felt tip pen. This can be made especially for the job or else a suitable hole may be drilled at the other end of a marking gauge stem.

The Panel Gauge Is no longer commercially available, so it has to be made. Both fence and stem are much longer. In the simple version, the stem is locked with a wedge. Screw locking can easily be arranged. This gauge often has the pencil facility too. Because of its long and rebated fence it cannot be rotated in the manner of the marking gauge, hence extra care and knack are required for its use.

The mortise gauge works similarly to the marking gauge but draws two parallel lines. It is indispensable for marking out mortise and tenon and also bridle joints. The spacing between the two points is adjusted either by a push rod or by a screw, the latter being preferred. This tool is generally made

Fig. 6.7 The mortise gauge.

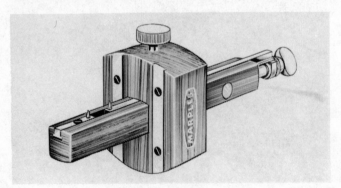

from a more exotic wood, such as rose-wood. On early models the fence was locked with a slot-headed screw. More recently, a thumb screw or a knurled knob has been supplied. The spacing of the points is not set to a rule but to the actual chisel, hand or machine, to be used. Set just a fraction below the points. This ensures a tightly-fitting tenon.

There are often occasions where the gauge mark or marks must be stopped short and not allowed to continue beyond a given line. Unlike pencil marks, the gauge marks cannot be rubbed out, so they are unwelcome on a polished sur-face. So, before gauging, stab in the point or points at the finished line. Then, when gauging normally, these holes can be felt and the gauge stopped.

In all cases the gauges operate on the push, not the pull. Experts swank by gauging in a number of exotic styles. For real accuracy, do not neglect to use the vice, particularly in the case of beginners. First learn to gauge well, then try the fancy holdings, if you must.

The Cutting Gauge As its name implies, this is fitted with a knife in place of the point. It has two distinct functions. One

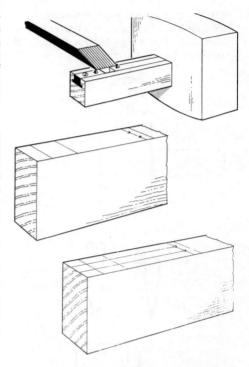

Fig. 6.8 Top, mortise gauge set to width of chisel. Centre, gauge stabbed in at end of line. Bottom, gauging stops short at the stabbing.

Fig. 6.9 The cutting gauge.

is marking across the grain, where it will not splinter, as in the case when marking dovetails. The other is the cutting of small rebates or narrow stringings.

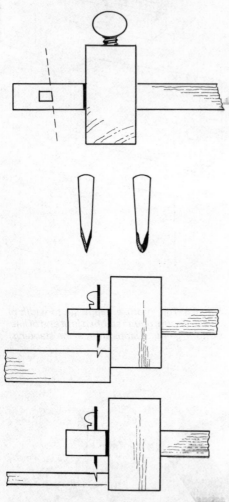

Fig. 6.10 Mortise angled for right-hander. 6.11. Cutter shapes, left for marking, right for heavy cutting. 6.12 Cutting a rebate, 6.13 Cutting a stringing.

The mark made by the knife has a vertical and a sloping side. The knife must be turned so that the vertical cut is part of the job while the sloping side is in the waste.

When bought, the cutting gauge can be improved by paring back the mortise at a slight angle (Fig. 6.10). This has the beneficial effect of pulling the gauge into the work, which is particularly helpful in cases where the grain of the wood has the tendency to throw the gauge out.

When the cutting gauge is used purely for marking purposes, a thin pointed blade is required. For heavier work when cutting rebates, a more rounded cutter should be fitted, with its bevel toward the fence. The same cutter suits the cutting of stringings, but for this, the bevel faces away from the fence.

The Marking Knife Lines to which one will later cut should be marked with a knife. The knife cut, unlike the pencil mark, has no thickness. The knife also serves to cleanly sever the fibres before sawing. A typical example would be the shoulder of a mortise and tenon joint.

There is a tradition, from which a few manufacturers are now escaping, of grinding the knife with a curved bevel on both sides. It is far better that it be ground on one side only, and at a slight angle, say 30° to 40°. It can then be sharpened in the same manner as a chisel.

In use, the knife is held vertically. The vertical side of the cut must be on the job. The sloping side is in the waste.

There is of course a left- and a right-handed version. If the wrong one is used, the bevel must be vertical while the knife is angled. This is sufficiently inconvenient to make it worthwhile for left handers to regrind their marking knives.

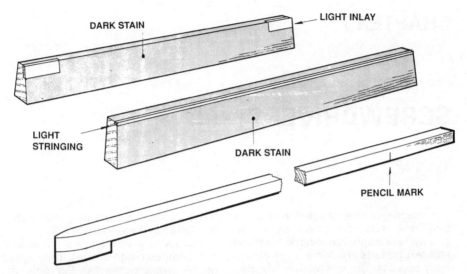

DARK STAIN

LIGHT INLAY

LIGHT STRINGING

DARK STAIN

PENCIL MARK

Fig. 6.14 At rear, winding strips with dark and light areas as an aid to sighting. Foreground, a diagonal-testing lath.

Winding strips are essential for the process of producing components to size. Their use was described on page 17. They cannot be bought therefore they must be made. Many variations are produced according to personal preference and available materials. The essential of all is that both strips should be truly parallel. An aid to sighting is achieved either by using dark and light woods or by masking and spraying. A convenient size for bench work is 15 × 1¾ in. For checking larger carcases when glueing up, about 32 × 2¼ in is suggested. The strips are often tapered in thickness to improve stability. Use only old, well seasoned timber, possibly reclaimed from furniture, for the construction of winding strips.

Diagonal laths can be improvised but tend to be required quickly when no suitable offcuts are to hand. As they fit well into a corner, they are more accurate than a steel tape and obviate errors of mismeasurement. The thickened end often enables the lath to span a cramp or other obstacle. Mark the diagonal lengths with a fine pencil and clean off after use. A wax or oil application will keep the pointed end free from glue.

CHAPTER 7

SCREWDRIVERS

The majority of work is still done using a traditional screwdriver on slot head screws, although cross-head patterns and fast threads are becoming increasingly popular. The screwdrivers for this work can be divided into four groups: the conventional rigid form, the simple ratchet, the spiral 'Yankee' pattern and the gimmicky models which appear from time to time with great advertising, then slowly fade away.

An old and well-tried shape is the cabinet pattern. These are quite scientifically planned with the length in proportion to the width of blade so as to apply the right amount of force to a given size of screw. Beware of the long 'electrician's' screwdriver. These are made to reach inaccessible screws.

Used on small screws they easily strip the thread in the wood.

Ratchet screwdrivers are made in a more limited range of sizes. They speed up the work somewhat but only the best have a really long life. They are particularly useful on jobs like hanging house doors where one hand is holding the work, making it difficult to change grip on a rigid screwdriver.

The spiral screwdriver, developed in the USA, is now widely copied in several sizes. Beware of the extremely poor versions. For the average worker it is doubtful whether their high price can be justified. They do offer a significant increase in torque and speed and, for the professional, the great advantage is on production work where large

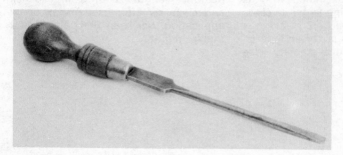

Fig. 7.1 Cabinet pattern screwdriver.

Fig. 7.2 Ratchet
screwdriver.

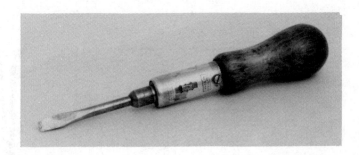

Fig. 7.3 (below)
spiral screwdriver.

numbers of identical screws are being
put into prepared holes. Various types
of bit are available, screwdriver, drill
and countersink. There is always the
danger of a spiral screwdriver bit slipping
out of the screw slot and damaging the
work, but a technique can be developed
of holding the screwhead and driver bit
together between thumb and forefinger
as you let the drive spring back, constantly re-centring the 'push'. There
are also cross-head screws, of course,
developed mainly for industry, which
necessitated suitable screwdrivers. The
first was the Phillips head, now obsolete
and succeeded by the Pozidriv which
has improved driving power and fast
threads. The screwdrivers for each of
these were slightly different.

Returning to the slot screwdriver,
while the blade should not be too thin,

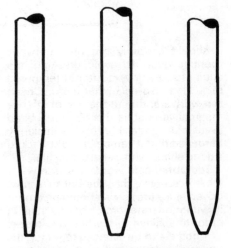

*Fig. 7.4 Blade taper on the left is the ideal for
a good quality tool. Centre is too stubby, right
even worse.*

Fig. 7.5

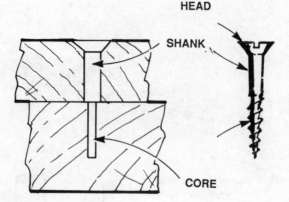

it should certainly not be stubby or rounded over. To avoid breaking, the ends of screwdrivers are not tempered to a high degree of hardness. Cheap screwdrivers, due to the use of inferior material, are not hard enough and bend in use. A good blade is sufficiently hardened that it can be brought back to a good shape with a sharp, fine file.

The American word 'Turnscrew' is more descriptive than the British 'screwdriver' since the screw should be turned in with moderate force, not driven in. In order to achieve this, when two pieces of wood are to be screwed together, the upper should be drilled to accept the shank of the screw with a frictionless fit. It may then be countersunk to leave the head minutely below the surface. The lower component is drilled to accept the core, leaving the threads to bite into the sides of the hole. A touch of grease to a

steel screw permits easy withdrawal at some later date. Beware of steel screws in oak. The acid in the oak will corrode the metal and additionally stain the wood dark blue in the neighbourhood. Because of the very high cost now of brass screws zinc plated ones are often used as a substitute. Other finishes are black japanned, chrome and bronze plated. Where it is not feasible to countersink, for example on very thin metal, round-headed screws are used.

A sufficient range of screwdrivers should be acquired to fit all the sizes of screws in common use. The blade must fit the slot of the screw both in thickness and in width. Too small a blade is liable to damage the screw slot, making further use difficult. Too large a blade will chew up the wood surrounding the countersinking. (See page 77 for drill sizes for woodscrews.)

CHAPTER 8

STRIKING TOOLS

The wide range of regional styles of hammer has now gone. The woodworker is left with two basic types – the Warrington pattern and the 'adze-eye' claw hammer. This latter is popular with carpenters, joiners and others engaged in constructional work. Its advantage is the claw for withdrawing nails. Many are nowadays steel-shafted. Cabinet makers and bench workers in general prefer the Warrington pattern with an ash or hickory shaft. Common sizes are an 8 oz for general bench work and nailing, and a 3 oz for pinning. The cross

pein of the Warrington hammer is also used for rubbing in inlay stringing and crossbanding.

Nails and pins are often concealed by punching and filling. Several nail punches are required with different sizes of end. It is worth paying a little more for a punch with a concave end as this will not slip off the nail. For marking metal for drilling, a centre punch is used. This has a pointed end ground at about 60°. Punches with a square striking end will not roll off the bench.

A useful tool of the past was the

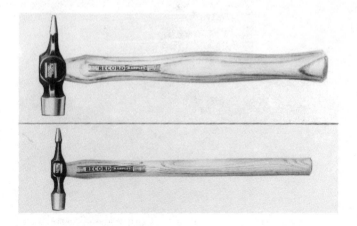

Fig. 8.1 The Warrington pattern general purpose hammer.

Fig. 8.2 Pin hammer, also Warrington pattern.

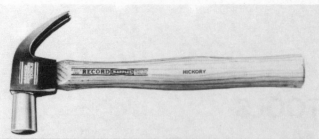

Fig. 8.3 The claw hammer, more the tool of the carpenter and joiner than of the cabinet-maker.

Fig. 8.4 Use of the claw hammer as a nail extractor. The wood block protects the work from bruising.

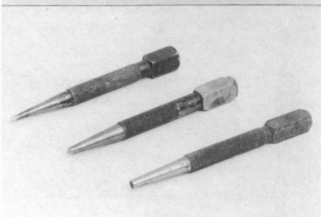

Fig. 8.5 Punches. Outer ones are small and large nail punches, centre a centre punch.

Fig. 8.6 Club or lump hammer, useful as a framing hammer.

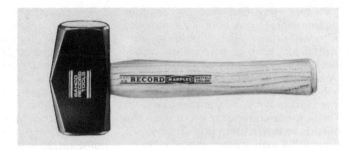

framing hammer, used to knock together the heavier mortise and tenon frames. It can be successfully replaced by the builder's club or lump hammer.

Hammer heads work loose and shafts have to be replaced. There are several methods of wedging them on, that is swelling out the top of the shaft to fit the tapered hole in the head. The following can be recommended.

Make a sawcut in the shaft along the length of the hammer head. Drive on the head until there is a slight projection. Tap in a wedge of dry, hard wood. When secure drive in a metal wedge at right angles to this. This can be bought or filed from a piece of mild steel. Finally smooth down to the hammer head using a file and perhaps a hacksaw.

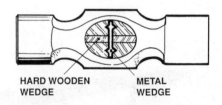

HARD WOODEN WEDGE   METAL WEDGE

Fig. 8.8 Wedging a hammer head.

Correct loose heads promptly. They are dangerous.

In addition to nailing, the hammer is used to tap joints together. Its small surface area enables the blow to be struck with precision. Work is protected from hammer marks by the use of a wood block.

Fig. 8.7 Hammer head fixing, showing metal and hardwood wedges.

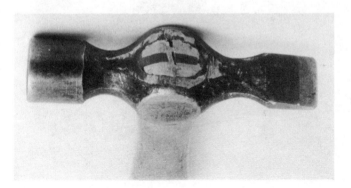

Pincers may conveniently be considered here since their sole purpose is to withdraw nails. Pliers, unsuitable for this job, have no place in the woodworking kit. The jaws of pincers must close well. The better tools are ground only on the inside of the jaws, permitting them to grip even a very small protrusion. Those more commonly ground on the outside as well cannot grip so close. To protect the work from damage, lever on a block of scrap wood.

The mallet has almost the sole purpose of driving chisels. It is not suitable for assembling joints since its large surface area, perhaps as great as 10 or 12 square inches, prohibits a really precise blow. It is often mistakenly thought that joints can be driven home by blows from the mallet without damage to the surface. This is just not true.

Several sizes are needed, as the mallet which drives in a ¾ in. mortise chisel will not be suitable on a fine drawer dovetail.

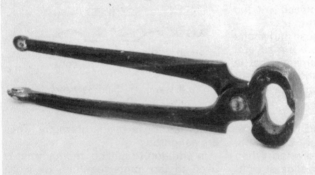

Fig. 8.9 Pincers. Note the bevel on the inside only of the jaws.

Fig. 8.10 A wood block should be used with pincers to protect work from bruising.

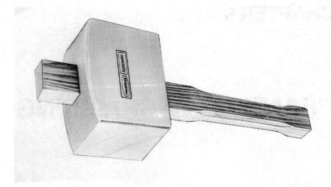

Fig. 8.11 Traditional English carpenter's mallet, available in a range of sizes and weights.

For fine work on the bench, the shaft of the average mallet is inconveniently long. Readers making their own mallets would do well to consider a shorter handle.

Many workers, especially for chopping out dovetails, prefer the round mallets of the carver. Two shapes are manufactured, in a variety of weights. For the gentler, close-up work these mallets have much to commend them. They can easily be turned from dense hardwood if access to a lathe is available.

Fig. 8.12 Round carver's mallet, favoured by many bench workers for light work such as chopping dovetails.

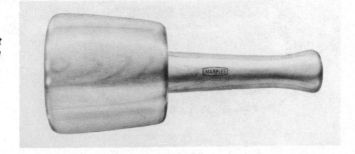

CHAPTER 9

CRAMPS AND CRAMPING

G cramps are universally used and they differ only in manufacturers' details. In North America they are known as C clamps. Cheaper versions, in cast aluminium alloy, are to be avoided since they break when pressure is applied.

The capacities run from 2 in. to a massive 12 in. G cramps are used for general glueing and laminating and also for holding work firm on the bench top when working it.

The use of a continental form of

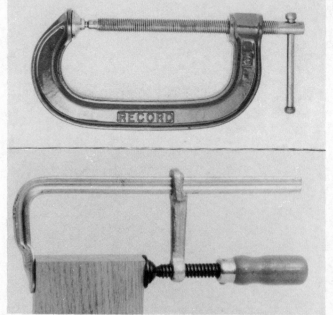

Fig. 9.1 The standard G cramp.

Fig. 9.2 Continental pattern adjustable cramp.

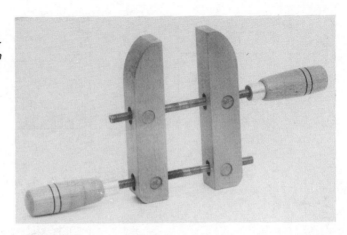

Fig. 9.3 Modern improved handscrews, at present more popular in North America than in Britain. Gives good pressure, will grip at extreme tips, holds tapered work and requires no cramping blocks.

threads are fast gaining ground and are much more common in North America. The handscrew and the wooden lever cam clamp, unlike all the others, do not require wood blocks to protect the work from damage. When working alone, the handling of work, cramps and wood blocks can be awkward.

The sash cramp is indispensable for pullling together frames and carcases. They vary in capacity from 18 in. to 78 in. There are two patterns with rectangular bars, 1¼ × ¼ in. and 1½ × 5/16 in. and two with T section bars, 1¾ × ¾ in and 2⅝ × ⅞ in. Extension bars are available for all.

sliding bar adjustable cramp is increasing. These cramps cover a wider range of sizes and are available in a light and a heavier form. For applying really heavy pressure the G cramp cannot be improved upon, but the continental pattern has a relatively deeper throat.

For lighter work, the wood and metal lever cam clamps are useful. They are light and cheap. This clamp is popular with model makers and musical instrument makers, whose work will not support heavy cramps.

The traditional handscrews are now more or less extinct but the modern fast-adjusting handscrews with metal

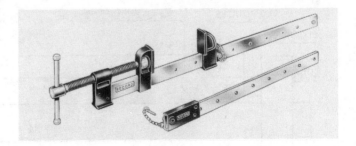

Fig. 9.4 Conventional sash cramp with extension bar. Heavier model with T-section bar is available.

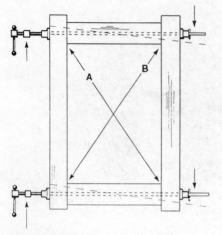

Fig. 9.5 Cramps are moved in the direction of the long diagonal.

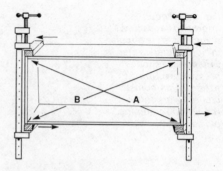

Fig. 9.7 If diagonal A is long, move the cramps in the direction shown.

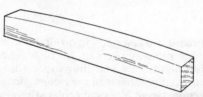

Fig. 9.8 Slightly curve cramping blocks to give pressure at the centre.

One cramp is generally of little use. When buying, choose two or, better still, four of the same size and pattern.

When glueing up a flat frame, the cramp bars must be positioned centrally beneath the rails. If on testing, the diagonals are found to be unequal, ie A is long and B is short, the cramps and their blocks are moved in the direction of the longer diagonal as shown. This should correct the diagonals.

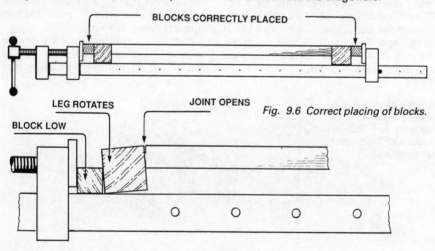

BLOCKS CORRECTLY PLACED

LEG ROTATES   JOINT OPENS   Fig. 9.6 Correct placing of blocks.

BLOCK LOW

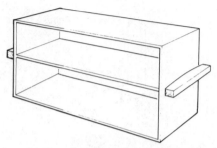

Fig. 9.9 Curved blocks are essential when cramping shelves or partitions.

In the end view, the pressure is directed by the cramping blocks along the centre line of the rail (Fig. 9.6). If the block is set low, as on the table shown, the component, in this case the leg, will rotate, causing the joint to open.

A carcase is cramped front and back, though for simplicity only the front is shown here. Cramping blocks for a carcase must extend for the full width of the job, be stout enough and be slightly curved to give pressure at the centre. This is essential when glueing in a central
shelf or partition where cramps can only grip near the edge.

The sash cramp is useful too, gripped in the bench vice, to hold shaped or tapered pieces for planing.

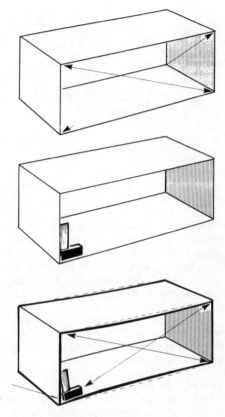

Fig. 9.11 Diagonals equal, carcase square. Try-square is inadequate for large carcases, especially as over-cramping creates false reading.

Fig. 9.10 Holding shaped or tapered components for planing.

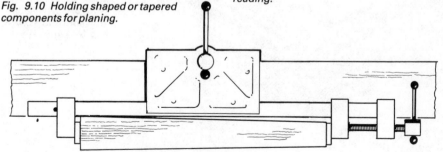

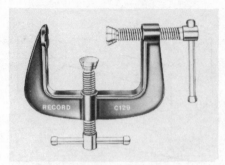

Fig. 9.12 Edging cramp useful for the application of hardwood lippings to plywood or edges to panels faced with plastic laminates.

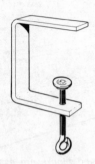

Fig. 9.13 A cheap and inefficient cramp form from strip metal usable for only the lightest of work.

The bench holdfast is designed specifically to hold down jobs on the bench while they are being worked. Modern holdfasts are supplied with steel bushes which, when let into the benchtop, prevent the hole from enlarging with use.

Light strip-metal cramps are a total waste of money. Pressure bends them out of shape. It is surprising in fact that anyone buys them.

THE BENCH VICE
When purchasing the vice, there is no doubt that the more money that can be afforded the better. The 7 in. model, measured along the length of the jaw, is really the minimum for serious work. The professional may wish to go to the larger size of 9 in. or 10½ in. There is a choice between quick release and plain screw models. If funds are short, go for the largest plain screw model which can be afforded. There is always a dearth of second-hand vices.

The range of Record vices seems to be supreme at the time of writing but there are several good rivals. Beware of imitation Records coming from the Far East. The vice is the single most expen-

Fig. 9.14 Popular bench vice by Record. Quick release model illustrated. Available with jaw widths of 7, 9 and 10½ in.

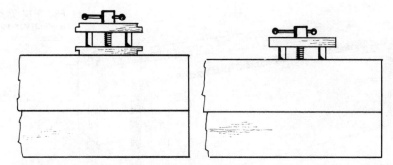

Fig. 9.15 There is a choice of flush jaw (on left) or projecting (right)

sive hand tool so one does not want to buy it twice. Keep it lightly lubricated and, from time to time, clean the thread.

Wood jaws are essential. Vices are given tapped holes for securing these. Check the thread. Record uses $\frac{5}{16}$ in. BSW (Whitworth). The choice is between a flush or a projecting inner jaw. Some workers will prefer to preserve the smooth line of the bench edge, to facilitate gripping long boards with the vice and an extra cramp. Against this is the argument for the projecting jaw, namely that the jaw is easily replaced when worn, that a sash cramp can easily be held in the manner of Fig. 9.10 and that both jaws can be rebated at the ends to accept auxiliary jaws. Whichever method is chosen, ensure that the inner faces are truly parallel, otherwise there will be holding difficulties.

It is useful if a lipping is fitted to the front or moving jaw. This not only gives protection to tools from the edge of the

Fig. 9.16 Vice jaws with modification for routing and attaching auxiliary jaws.

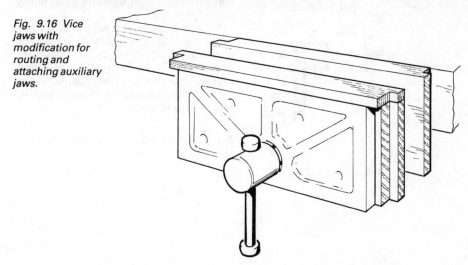

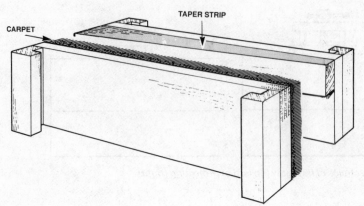

CARPET

TAPER STRIP

Fig. 9.17 Types of auxiliary jaws for vices.

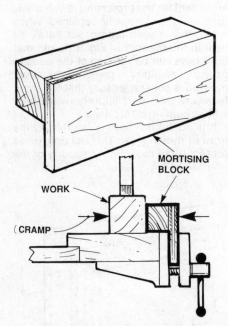

MORTISING
BLOCK

WORK

CRAMP

metal jaw but is also a useful aid for power routing.

Glue on a slip, say ½ in. thick, and plane level with the bench top. Run the fence of the power router along the inside of the jaw taking a cut from the outer edge of the lipping. This is now truly parallel with the inner face of the jaw. Small components can now be held in the vice for grooving etc, the router running against the lipping. Small pieces can similarly be grooved by hand using a plough plane.

Auxiliary jaws are easily made from multi-ply and can solve a variety of problems. Two of the most useful are carpet-lined jaws for holding polished work and a jaw with an applied taper strip for conveniently gripping matched tapered components.

Fig. 9.18 (left). Use of a mortising block in vice, also mentioned on page 43.

CHAPTER 10

DRILLING AND BORING

The simplest boring tools are the *bradawl*, sharpened on both sides, using an oilstone to obtain a keen edge, and the *awl*. The most useful awl is the tapered square awl which has four cutting edges. Both are commonly used for making screw holes, a task nowadays increasingly performed with a hand drill and an assortment of wood drills. The gimlet is virtually extinct among serious woodworkers.

A distinction should now be made between a bit and a drill. In general terms, a drill is an engineer's tool designed for use on metal, while a bit is made specifically for wood. Again generally, a drill has a round shank and is held in a three jaw chuck. A bit has a square shank and is held in the two jaw chuck of a brace. Machine bits, intended for three jaw chucks, naturally have round shanks.

All woodcutting bits have three features in common. These are a needle point, which permits the bit to start precisely on the required spot, and a spur or nicker which severs the fibres in advance of the router or cutter, which removes the waste within the scribed circle.

The twist drill lacks the needle point

Fig. 10.1, top, the bradawl. 10.2, centre, carpenter's brace. 10.3, bottom, a hand-drill of superior quality with engineering-type chuck and key, ball thrust race etc.

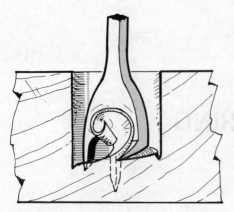

Fig. 10.4 Cutting action embodying the three basic drill features.

and spur. Its stubby point makes accurate starting uncertain. Nevertheless, it is now the main implement for drilling pilot and clearance holes for wood-screws. The electric drill must now be accepted as a hand tool, doing much of the work formerly done with the hand drill.

The centre bit is the basic form of woodboring bit having the three features

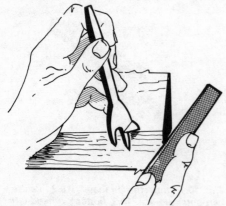

Fig. 10.6 Support the bit on a wood block when sharpening the cutter edge.

described and nothing else. Its purpose is boring shallow holes or through holes in thin wood. To avoid bursting out, commence boring from the second side as soon as the point is visible. Sadly, this excellent bit is disappearing from the catalogues.

Sharpen with a fine file, filing the spur only on the inside to avoid reducing the diameter. The router is filed on the top side only, maintaining the maker's angle. Only very occasionally will the point need attention.

The successor, the *fast cutting centre bit*, has a screw nose to pull in the bit without heavy pressure being necessary.

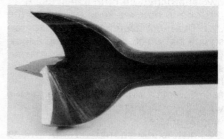

Fig. 10.5 Conventional centre bit.

Coarse and fine threads were manu-factured for use on softwoods and hard-woods respectively but one is seldom given the choice. In hardwoods the larger sizes are heavy work since they pull in rather quickly. The spur and router are sharpened similarly. If a centre bit is used for deep holes, it will wander off line.

For deep holes, several patterns of twist or auger bits were developed. They have the screw nose with a fine point, one or two spurs and one or two routers. The characteristic twist serves two purposes. It acts as a guide, preventing the bit from wandering off

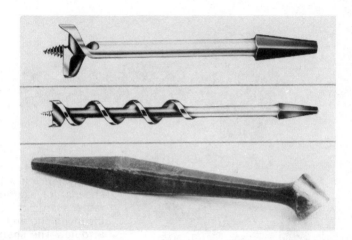

Fig. 10.6 Modern fast-cutting centre bit. Sizes ¼ to 2¾ in., lengths 4–6 in.

Fig. 10.7 Solid centre auger bit, commonly termed twist bit. Sizes ¼ to 1½ in., lengths 8–10 in.

Fig. 10.8 Traditional Snail head counter-sink for wood.

line and also as an inclined plane up which the waste is discharged. A shorter version is the dowel bit.

The countersink bit is available in two forms. The more common rose head is primarily intended for metal. For the woodworker this means such tasks as deepening the countersinking in hinges and fittings. Round shank models are made for use in the hand- or electric drill. The true countersink for wood is the snail head. Its single (or occasionally double) cutter is kept sharp to quite a keen edge with a fine round file, working as always on the inside.

The forstner bit runs virtually without a centre, on its circumference. It is intended for shallow holes but will also cut part holes near an edge. Sharpening on the inside edge of the circumference is tedious, hence woodworkers tend to use this bit sparingly. For machine and electric drill work this has been replaced by the saw tooth bit. Both are quite expensive.

The gimlet-, spoon-, shell- and nose-bits still featured in some textbooks are virtually obsolete.

Two bits have been developed for high speed work in electric drills. The

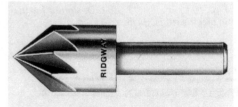

Fig. 10.9 Rose head countersink, round shank for hand or electric drill. Square made.

Fig. 10.10 Small forstner bit is now becoming obsolescent.

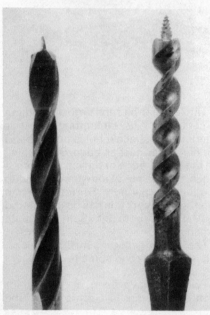

flatbit is in fact more of a scraper than a cutter, hence it will not perform at low speeds, for example in a brace. It has rather a large point, which is sometimes inconvenient, and a scraper rather than a router. The sharp corners of this act as spurs. Sharpening is done in a small metalwork vice with a fine file, preserving the maker's angle.

The wood drill or lip and spur drill looks superficially like the metal twist drill. Closer observation reveals that it has been ground to produce a sharp point and two spurs. The waste is removed by an action midway between cutting and scraping. These drills are difficult to sharpen but being generally quite hard, keep their edges well. They are available mainly in metric, down to quite small sizes. The larger sizes have their round shanks reduced to ¼ in diameter.

For really large though not deep holes,

Fig. 10.12. Left, lip and spur wood drill. Right, dowel bit.

Fig. 10.13 (below). Flatbit. Designed for use in electric drills. Sizes ¼–1½ in.

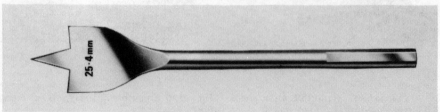

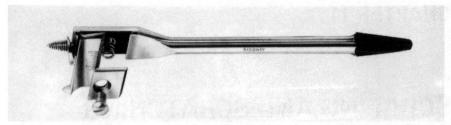

Fig. 10.14 The expansive bit for large, shallow holes.

the expansive bit is manufactured, generally supplied with two sizes of cutter. This will cope with holes up to a diameter of 4 in. or even 6 in. or so the makers claim. In hardwood it is extremely hard work, made a little easier if the ratchet of the brace is set to use only the pulling part of the swing. This is quite an expensive tool. Much of its work can now be done easier and better by a small power router.

The brace and the hand drill are too familiar and simple to require any further descriptions. They are rapidly giving way to the electric drill though, for the itinerant craftsman cut off from a power source, they are of course indispensable.

DRILLING SIZES FOR WOODSCREWS

Screw Gauge	Clearance Hole		Pilot Hole	
	ins	mm	ins	mm
2	$3/32$	2.5	$1/16$	1.5
4	$7/64$	3	$5/64$	2
6	$9/64$	3.5	$5/64$	2
8	$11/64$	4.5	$3/32$	2.5
10	$13/64$	5	$1/8$	3
12	$15/64$	6	$1/8$	3

CHAPTER 11

SCRAPING AND SCRATCHING AND ABRASIVE TOOLS

Wood can be removed in either of two ways – by cutting or by scraping. Fig. 11.1 shows the cleaving action of an axe. You will see that the cutting edge, for the most part, is clear of the wood. The action of the chisel and the plane is somewhat similar; the wood splits ahead of the cutting edge, with the result that the edge is fairly long-lasting. But in the scraping action (Fig. 11.2) the edge is in constant and heavy contact with the timber, so it blunts very quickly.

In addition, cutting requires less effort than scraping, and sharpening takes less time. So it is obvious that cutting is to be preferred whenever possible. Scraping should generally be considered as a last resort or a special case – but it does have one great advantage: it never tears the grain.

When opting for scraping, take care that the tool works at its maximum efficiency. In fact 'scraping' is an unfortunate word, because it leads people to accept a very low standard of performance.

The Cabinet Scraper The cabinet scraper is a rectangular piece of tempered steel

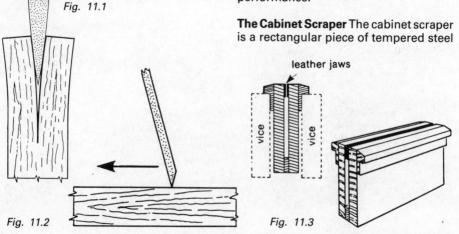

Fig. 11.1

Fig. 11.2

leather jaws

vice

vice

Fig. 11.3

varying between 3 × 1½ in. and 6 × 2¾ in. 5 × 2½ in. is perhaps the most convenient size. Very flexible scrapers are easy to use but get very hot. A thick, rigid one stays cooler but is tiring on the fingers. Having some special equipment for sharpening makes sure that the job is well done rather than a hasty touch-up.

Fig. 11.4 High speed steel burnisher.

Fig. 11.3 shows a set of vice jaws which not only make the filing easier, but also reduce the amount of unpleasant noise which can result. Arrange things so that when the leather linings are in place, the jaws are naturally open just a little more than the scraper's thickness.

Do not stint on the file. Buy a 10 in. or, better still, a 12 in. single-cut millsaw file. Make a fine polished handle for the file, which is kept in a plastic sleeve and used exclusively for sharpening scrapers. An oilstone is the next tool required. While any fine (not superfine) artificial stone will serve, a small circular axe stone is most suitable. A 3 in. diameter Carborundum pattern is available, with a fine and a medium side. A fine lubricating oil is used with it. Lastly, a burnisher is required. All sorts of things are pressed into service here, from the backs of gouges to ground-off files. But, if the material is not hard enough, grooves will eventually be formed in it, and then the finest edge will not be attainable. Ideally purchase an engineer's round lathe toolbit 4 in. long by ¼ or 5/16 in. diameter, in high-speed steel. Eclipse and several other firms make these. The cost is not excessive, considering the tool is for a lifetime. Once again, make a nicely polished handle for it, and keep it wrapped in a rag or plastic sleeve.

Sharpening the cabinet scraper is a procedure often described, but there are several features worth pointing out specially.

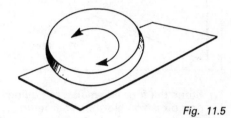

Fig. 11.5

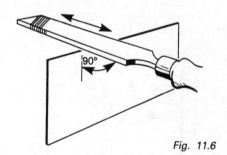

Fig. 11.6

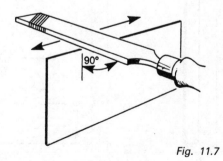

Fig. 11.7

79

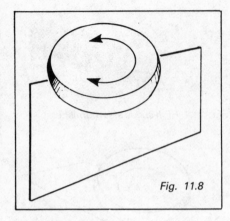

Fig. 11.8

(1) Stone the four edges flat, removing any burr from former sharpenings (Fig. 11.5).
(2) Set up in the bench vice in the scraper jaws and file straight and square, removing all trace of former edges (Fig. 11.6).

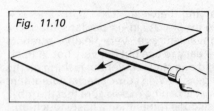

Fig. 11.10

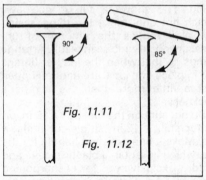

Fig. 11.11

Fig. 11.12

90°

85°

(3) Finish by draw-filing, still keeping the file square to the scraper (Fig. 11.7).
(4) Repeat this with the stone to remove any file marks (Fig. 11.8).
(5) Repeat these procedures on the other long edge.
(6) Remove any burr by stoning (Fig. 11.5). There are now two long edges trued to 90° in section, as in Fig. 11.9.

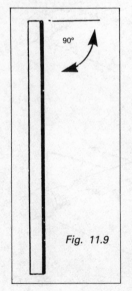

90°

Fig. 11.9

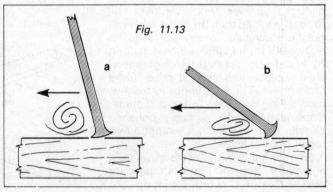

Fig. 11.13

a

b

(7) Lightly oil the burnisher and burnish the faces flat (Fig. 11.10).

(8) Return to the special jaws and burnish the edge with a few firm strokes at exactly 90°. This produces edges in section as in Fig. 11.11.

(9) Repeat at an angle of about 85°, producing the cutting edge in section as in Fig. 11.12.

Fig. 11.13a shows the cutting position when sharpened as described. In Fig. 11.13b too much angle has been given in the burnishing, with the result that the tool only cuts when held at an inconveniently low angle. In use, cut *not* as Fig. 11.14a or Fig. 11.14b but as 11.14c, with a slicing action.

To obtain shavings of a manageable width, bend the tool by thumb pressure. Some workers tape up their thumbs with surgical tape as protection when the scraper becomes hot. Note that the scraper should be taking off shavings – thin and curling, If only dust is made, it needs resharpening. But *beware!* A flat planed surface can easily be upset by

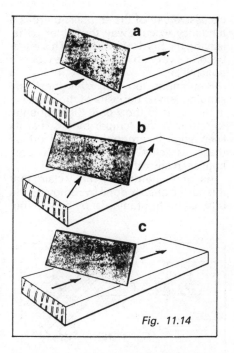

Fig. 11.14

Fig. 11.15 The cabinet scraper in use.

excessive use of the scraper; there is a tendency to cut away the softer parts, leaving the harder parts high. This effect becomes very obvious once the wood is polished.

Remember, too, that even the finest sanding leaves deposits of the abrasive in the pores of the wood. Subsequently to return to the scraper means that its keen edge is promptly ground off by these particles. (The same of course applies to any other cutting edge.)

As for re-sharpening, many claim that this can be quickly done by removing the burr, either by stoning or by burnishing,

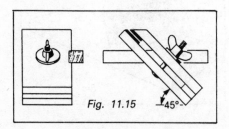

Fig. 11.15

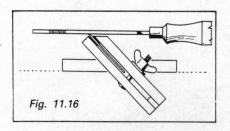

Fig. 11.16

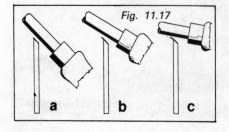

Fig. 11.17

a   b   c

and then burnishing the edge in the normal way. Each time, of course, the burnishing angle must be increased – until the angle of working (Fig. 11.13b) becomes inconvenient. On balance the moments saved by avoiding making a brand-new cutting edge are not worth-while. If the file, stone and burnisher are stored readily to hand, most readers will prefer to do the job properly each time.

After a long interval, shaped scrapers are again becoming available. But it is always possible to file or grind a small scraper to any convenient curve. These curved scrapers are also useful for face-plate work on the lathe: for example, when removing circular marks from the inside of a bowl. The work must be stationary, preferably with the faceplate held in the bench vice.

The Scraper Plane Over the years numerous attempts have been made to ease the strain on the fingers by fitting the scraper into some form of plane body. The simplest, most common and very effective model is the scraper plane made by Stanley. Superficially this looks like a giant spokeshave, but there the similarity ends. The flat sole ensures that the surface remains true, but the length is short enough to permit local cleaning-up. The cut is adjustable by bending the blade with a thumbscrew.

The scraper-plane blade is sharpened differently from the cabinet scraper. The filing angle is not 90° but 45°, which necessitates a different holding device. The one illustrated in Fig. 11.15 makes it easy to file at 45° by keeping the file horizontal. A pair of jaws is made, the space between the leather strips giving an easy fit to the blade. The jaws are closed by a bolt and wing-nut. One jaw only is glued and screwed to a horizontal strip; the other is free to move. When the jaws are dropped into the bench vice the blade is held firmly at 45°.

To sharpen, first stone off any old edge as in Fig. 11.5. Now file the bevel as in Fig. 11.16. Stone off the filing burr, stone out the file marks, and again remove any burr – in other words, sharpen like a plane iron, but at 45°. Repeat on the opposite edge.

Now remove the blade from the jaws and lay flat on the bench. Burnish the flat side as in Fig. 11.10. Keep the burnisher absolutely flat (and of course lightly oiled). Next hold the blade upright in the bench vice and burnish as follows – Fig.11.17. Lay on the burnisher at just over 45° and give a firm stroke (Fig. 11.17a). Lift the burnisher to about 60° and give a firm but heavier stroke (Fig. 11.17b). Finally, holding the burnisher at 80°, give one firmer and heavier stroke (Fig. 11.17c). The edge is now sharp and fit for use. Repeat on the other edge.

Carefully insert the blade into the stock, making sure that the three screws are slack and that the cutting edges are kept clear of metal. The flat side of the blade leans forward; the bevel is towards the adjusting screw. Stand the plane on a flat piece of wood and press the blade firmly down. Hold it there by tightening the two clamping screws. In this position the tool may cut finely or not at all. The cut is obtained or increased by the use of the central screw. The more this is turned, the more the blade is bent and the thicker (but narrower) the shaving. Use the scraper plane in the same manner as the hand scraper – that is, parallel with the grain but with a skew or slicing cut (Fig. 11.14c).

When the scraper plane refuses to cut, the cause is generally as shown in Fig. 11.18; the burnisher has been applied at too square an angle, with the result that (as shown at X) the actual cutting edge is not in contact with the wood.

Bear in mind that the spare edge can harm the unwary, particularly in school and evening-class workshops, so it is advisable to cover it with surgical or carpet tape.

The Scratch Tool From the Middle Ages until comparatively recent times the scratch tool (often called a scratch stock) was the main means of making mouldings. It is still a most useful tool for small mouldings, beadings, rebates and grooves, particularly grooves for inlaying.

In essence it is a small scraper plane with a shaped cutter. Until the final cuts,

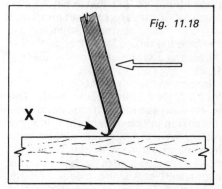

Fig. 11.18

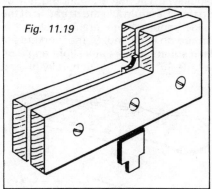

Fig. 11.19

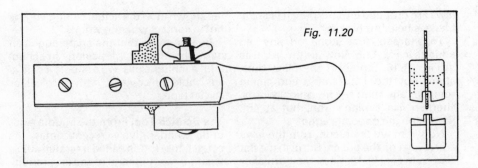

Fig. 11.20

it works best with the cutter leaning forward slightly, so the sole should be slightly rounded. Fig. 11.19 shows the commonly accepted form of scratch stock – but a tool like that in Fig. 11.20 is much more convenient to set and use. It is much easier to make small adjustments to the sliding fence than to slacken the screws and adjust the cutter. See Fig. 11.21.

Ideally cutters are made from $5/8 \times 1/16$ in. ground flat tool steel. This is readily available from good tool merchants in convenient short lengths. Alternatives are several: pieces sawn from hand scrapers or old handsaws, power hacksaw blades (carbon steel, not high-speed steel) and pieces of large bandsaws. The material should not be too thin. Carefully file the negative of the shape required; generally a shape is formed on each end. Some workers file dead square, others at a slight angle of, say, 10–15°. The angle generally gives a

better cut, while the square edge will cut both backwards and forwards. After filing, stone the faces flat.

If it is necessary to harden the cutter, heat it to bright red and then quench it in water or, better still, in oil. It will now be much too hard for re-sharpening. To temper it, brighten one face with emery cloth, place it on a larger piece of metal and gently warm it with a gas torch until the colours begin to appear. When light brown is reached, quench rapidly. The cutter will now keep a good edge, but it can still be filed.

ABRADING TOOLS

In shaped places where the spokeshave cannot reach, the woodworker is forced back on the use of files. For rapid removal of wood the rasp is used. Half round is the most convenient generally and the most easily obtainable. Round is also manufactured. The coarsest is termed the wood rasp while a finer model is known as the cabinet rasp. Nowadays only a limited range of sizes is manufactured.

For finer work there is the wood file, also available in half round and round form. The coarsest is termed bastard and a finer, second cut. In the event of wood files not being obtainable, metalwork files of the same grades can be

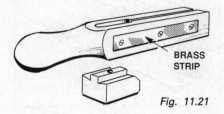

BRASS STRIP

Fig. 11.21

Fig. 11.22 From the top, wood rasp, cabinet rasp and wood file.

used, but they must be relatively new. Files of the finer grades clog and so are unsuitable for woodwork. Wood files should be kept clean by the use of a steel wire brush, particularly when resinous wood is being worked.

There is continuous development of throwaway abrading tools of the nutmeg grater type. These tend to be aimed at the do-it-yourself market and do not find much favour with serious craftsmen. They do not perform particularly well on end grain. For serious work they are no substitute, as their makers claim, for the plane.

ABRASIVE PAPERS

A piece of abrasive paper consists of many thousands of minute scrapers, which become blunt like any other type of scraper. It is the last tool to be applied to the work before polishing. Although the words sanding and sander are in common use, sandpaper as such has long since been extinct. The abrasive papers commonly used by the woodworker are the following.

GLASSPAPER, literally glass crystals glued to strong brown paper. The grades are traditionally known as Flour, 00, 0, 1, 1½, Fine 2, Middle 2, Strong 2. Glasspaper blunts quickly and is not now much used by woodworkers except for the flour grade during the polishing process.

FLINT PAPER, made from a natural material, was not greatly better than glasspaper and is now largely superseded by improved papers. The grades are termed 4/0, 3/0, 2/0, 0, ½, 1, 1½, 2, 2½ and 3.

GARNET PAPER, consisting of crushed garnet, is one of the most successful of the modern papers. It is an economical paper, most preferred by cabinet makers since it gives a good finish with a reasonably long life. It is produced as 'close coat' for hand sanding and 'open coat' for power sanding. Open coat is popular for woodturning and performs best on resinous material. Garnet paper is graded in the much more intelligible grit sizes, ie the mesh size per square inch. 180 is quite fine, comparable to flour glasspaper. 60 is coarse enough for most hand work and power sanders. 240 may be used for cutting back polishes.

ALUMINOUS OXIDE, also known as Aloxite, is a harder and more durable cutting material, suitable for both wood and metal. In practice it tends to be used mainly for machine sanding. It too is graded in grit sizes.

SILICA CARBIDE PAPER is commonly known as 'wet or dry'. It is the hardest grit and provides the most expensive papers. This is little used for working on wood but the finer grades, used wet with water or white spirit, are excellent for cutting back between coats during the

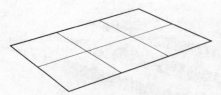

Fig. 11.23 Cut or tear a sheet of glass-paper into six to fit commercial cork blocks.

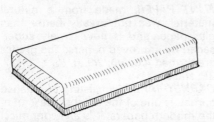

Fig. 11.24 A carpet-faced block is useful in the polishing process.

polishing process. Only the finer grades are used for this purpose, say 400 or 800. These papers are graded up to 1200.

Sanding is a process which should be undertaken as seriously as planing and well-used, blunt paper should be discarded. The standard sheet should be halved lengthwise and then each half divided into three. Lay the sheet on a flat surface, abrasive down, then cut by scoring heavily along a straight-edge with a scriber or compass point. This gives six pieces which perfectly fit commercial sanding blocks with no waste. These blocks are of cork and measure about 4 × 2½ × 1 in. Blocks can be made by glueing up layers of cork flooring tiles or by glueing one such on to a wood block. Wood only blocks tend to wear the paper through quickly, especially at the corners. For cutting back in the polishing process a useful block is made from wood faced with thick carpet.

Special care must be given when sanding edges and corners lest they become rounded over. Aggressively sharp corners however should be slightly softened. Test by rubbing along the corners, not the thumb or fingertips, but the clenched knuckles. Sanding must always follow the grain to avoid scratches. However grits, if 240 and finer, can safely be used in any direction, a clear advantage when dealing with mitres, veneers, inlays, marquetry or very difficult woods. After sanding, cutting tools should not be re-introduced. The grain has become filled with minute abrasive crystals which will rapidly destroy the keen edge of the tool. A handbrush should be constantly used during sanding operations and when working irritant woods, a dust mask should be worn. Workers with allergic symptoms are advised to wear one for all sanding operations.

A useful job in the closing minutes of the working day is to glue slips of abrasive paper to small wood offcuts and dowels to make in effect glasspaper files which often prove handy for getting into awkward places. Some papers can be glued back-to-back providing stiff slips, often useful in turning and cleaning up mouldings.

APPENDIX 1

THE BENCH

There can be few subjects upon which woodworkers will disagree more than the bench. However, for readers with no very definite or strongly-held views, the following is suggested as a good general purpose bench, economical, straightforward in construction and comfortable to work at.

The underframing, from 4 × 3 timber, is mortised and tenoned together. Good clean softwood is quite adequate though hardwood may of course be used at added cost.

The top must be of hardwood of a minimum thickness of 2 in. (50 mm) and as dry as possible. The back rail may be of softwood but must be of an equal thickness. Both these components are rebated to accept the well board. Do not use softwood for this since, after a

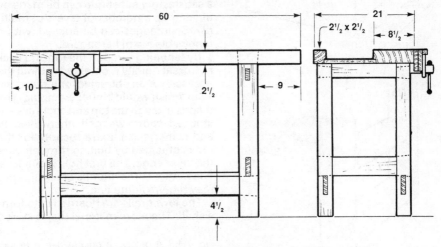

Fig. A1.1 A basic workbench. Under-framing should be from 4×3 in. nominal.

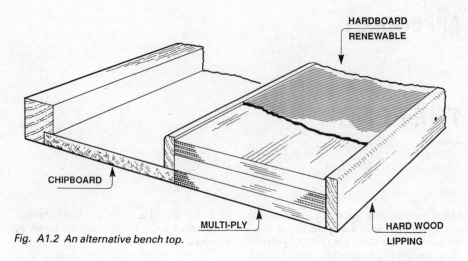

HARDBOARD
RENEWABLE

CHIPBOARD

MULTI-PLY

HARD WOOD
LIPPING

Fig. A1.2 An alternative bench top.

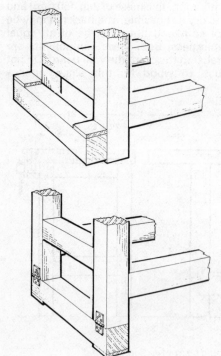

number of years in the dry, some soft-woods flake. These flakes can easily catch under the fingernails when picking out tools – quite a painful experience. Blockboard, plywood or chipboard are more suitable.

If a hardwood top cannot be obtained, a satisfactory substitute can be made by glueing up a number of layers of multi-ply. Solid edges can be applied, with a renewable top of hardboard.

By tenoning through the top and back rail, great rigidity is obtained without the necessity of an obtrusive long rail at the front which would hinder cramping. The tenons through the top and back rails are stopped short, wedged, then filled in and planed flush. Extra security for the top is obtained by bolting through near the inner edge. The bolt hole is similarly filled. After some months of use this nut may require tightening.

The lower rails are boarded in to form a shelf. The more material that is stored

Fig. A1.3 A device to raise a bench to suit differing heights of workers.

here the better since it gives added solidity to the bench.

In a communal workshop, where benches are used by workers of widely differing heights, hinged blocks (Fig. A1.3) give a choice of two heights.

The vice, with rebated ends and a routing strip, has been previously described. Left-handers will, of course, fit their vices on the right-hand end of the bench. The following holding system is most strongly recommended.

A tail vice is used which has the customary wooden jaws. The moving jaw is fitted with one which is extra thick. This is grooved to take a sliding hardwood dog. The metal jaw is tapped to take a thumbscrew. A sheet metal clip protects the dog from the screw. Quite a light, cheap vice can be adapted for the purpose. A new vice, fitted by the makers with a sliding metal dog is both heavy and expensive.

A recent development on these lines has been the introduction by Record of a combined light tail vice and planing grip at quite an economical price. This should work well in combination with the system described, which itself is far more efficient than merely a series of holes in the bench top.

The bench edges are grooved and fitted each side with a metal strip of 3 × ⅛ in. (20 × 3 mm). In addition to the countersunk holes for the screws, the strip is drilled ¼ in. (6 mm) at regular intervals. This spacing must be comfortably less than the amount of movement of the tail vice. The planing stop-bar has two cranked arms riveted to it, the inner one being hammered tight and rigid, the outer one less so, allowing a small amount of tight rotation. Short ¼ in. (6 mm) steel pegs are brazed or silver soldered to the ends. These should fit comfortably into the steel strips. Before finally screwing fast the steel strips, check that the stop-bar is quite square to the bench front.

The stop-bar can be drilled and countersunk underneath to permit the attachment of shaped wood blocks to hold curved, circular or irregularly shaped pieces. Thick components are catered for by inserting a wood block under the stop-bar.

Fig. A1.4. The tail vice by Record is a possible alternative to adapting a cheap one.

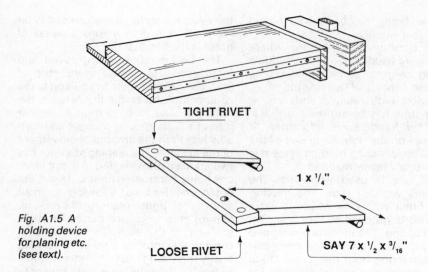

TIGHT RIVET

1 x ¹/₄"

Fig. A1.5 A holding device for planing etc. (see text).

LOOSE RIVET

SAY 7 x ¹/₂ x ³/₁₆"

Two drawers hung from the bench top are handy for small tools and accessories. They must close, say 6 in. from the bench edge to permit cramps and hand-screws to be used.

A useful holdfast of the type illustrated can be simply made and fitted to the bench. Drill three or four ½ in (13 mm) holes through the bench top, counterbore underneath and crush into each a ½ in. BSW nut. Screwed rod to suit makes the clamping and tensioning screws. In use, tighten the clamp screw until the wooden arm is level, then apply pressure with the handled screw. The holes not in use are filled with short dowels.

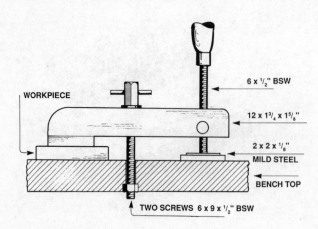

WORKPIECE

6 x ¹/₂" BSW

12 x 1³/₄ x 1⁵/₈"

2 x 2 x ¹/₈"
MILD STEEL

BENCH TOP

TWO SCREWS 6 x 9 x ¹/₂" BSW

Fig. A1.6 Suggested sizes for a bench holdfast.

APPENDIX 2

SHOOTING BOARDS

These are a considerable improvement on the conventional models in that the stop block cannot be worn by misuse, causing spelching, and the plane cannot be held at a wrong angle. They are both left- and right handed so that components with a moulded corner can always be planed into the moulding, again avoiding spelching. Sizes are only suggestions. Very small shooting boards accepting a block plane are useful for fine work.

THE 90° SHOOTING BOARD
Start with the multi-ply base. On to this is screwed a runner made from acrylic sheet. Offcuts of this may be obained from makers of illuminated signs. Alternatively two thicknesses of plastic laminate, such as Formica, may be glued together. A gripping strip for the vice is screwed and glued to the lower face.

Two end blocks are made from hardwood to suit the plane width. The two

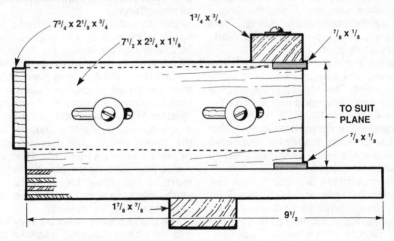

Fig. A2.1 90° shooting board, end view.

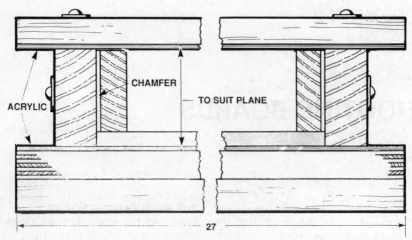

CHAMFER

ACRYLIC

TO SUIT PLANE

27

Fig. A2.2 90° shooting board, side view.

front corners are cut out to accept the runners. Two ¼ in. (6 mm) slots are worked in the block to take screws.

The end blocks are now glued and screwed to the base. Check that they are square to the runner using a draughtsman's large set-square and holding a block tightly against the runner. This is more accurate than the average workshop try-square.

Prepare a top rail from sound, dry hardwood and similarly screw to it the upper runner. This should project about ¹⁄₁₆ in. (2 mm). The rail is then screwed in place with a No. 10 or 12 round head screw and a large diameter washer. This operates through a slightly elongated hole to allow slight adjustment, hence this joint is not glued.

A loose platform is made from ½ in. (12 mm) multi-ply or M.D.F. (medium density hardboard) to fit between the end blocks and is rebated to fit over the runner. Secure with a few well countersunk screws.

Now test for accuracy as follows. Saw off the corner from a small plastic try-square until it will freely pass under the top rail. Hold a plane firmly against the two runners and check for 90° between plane and platform, adjusting the top rail as necessary.

The thrust blocks are made to fit against the end blocks with a sliding fit. These also are secured with No. 10 or 12 r.h. woodscrews and large washers.

Hold the plane firmly in place and test that the thrust blocks are square to it with the large set-square. If accurately prepared they should still be square but, if not, correct by careful planing. Move the thrust blocks just forward of the runners and screw up firmly. Then plane with a fine cut until the plane will cut no more. If the thrust blocks do become worn, advance them then again plane until the plane ceases to cut.

The blade must always be very sharp. It is recommended that a special blade be kept for shooting board work, ground

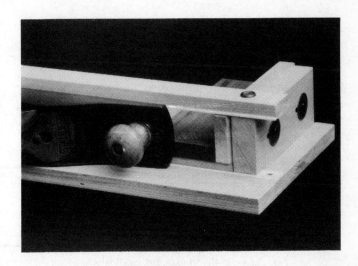

Fig. A2.3 Method of use, showing work-piece and thrust block.

and sharpened completely square.

A hanging hole will help reduce knocks which could render the board inaccurate.

For planing mitres, as for example on picture frames, a 45° block can be added when required. This must be made from glued together layers of multi-ply since solid wood may shrink, rendering the angle incorrect. Again, round-head screws with large washers are preferred, passing through short slots which will allow adjustment for wear. With a 45° set-square check the angles between block and plane sole. There is no problem of spelching when cutting wood at 45°, hence no thrust blocks are needed.

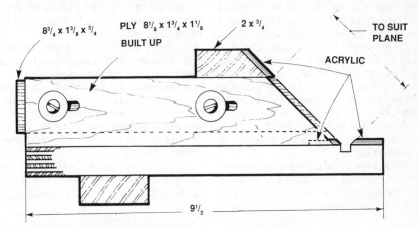

$8^3/_4$ x $1^3/_8$ x $^3/_4$ PLY $8^1/_8$ x $1^3/_4$ x $1^1/_8$ 2 x $^3/_4$ TO SUIT PLANE
BUILT UP

ACRYLIC

$9^1/_2$

Fig. A2.4 45° shooting board, end view.

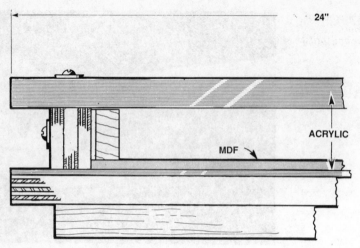

Fig. A2.5 45° shooting board, side view.

THE MITRE SHOOTING BOARD

A similar baseboard is produced with its gripping bar underneath. A groove of ¼ × ¼ in. is cut near one edge and the two lower runners are screwed on. They have been angled at 45° before fixing.

The end blocks are made, but this time they must be built up from layers of multi-ply to avoid shrinkage, which would increase the 45° angle. Cut one end of each at 45°, saw notches to take the runners and cut the screw slots. Screw on the end blocks but do not glue, checking for squareness with the outer runner. Fit the top runner to the top rail then screw this in place with No. 10 or 12 screws and washers through an elongated hole.

Add the loose platform and the thrust blocks, then test for accuracy. Hold a plane firmly against the runners and check for squareness of the end blocks with a large set-square. If all is well, unscrew, glue with a slower-setting glue, such as Cascamite, then rescrew the end blocks. Having quickly returned the top rail, check again for 45° between the platform and the plane sole.

Replace the thrust blocks, checking again for squareness. If not quite square, adjust by gently planing.

On both shooting boards, the outer end of the thrust blocks should be chamfered to prevent splitting off.

A refinement is that the top rails may be more firmly secured by using a cylindrical nut with a machine screw and washer in place of the large woodscrew. On the 90° board the top rail may be rebated for the runner.

Acrylic sheet can be planed and sawn either by hand or machine. The runners are best planed screwed to a board.

INDEX

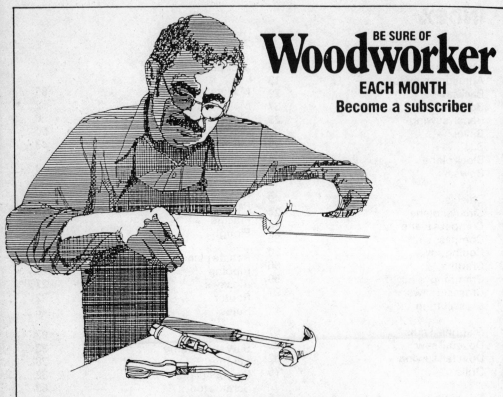